D1130641

BOOKS BY

*PRUDENCIO DE PEREDA*

WINDMILLS IN BROOKLYN *1960*

FIESTA *1953*

ALL THE GIRLS WE LOVED *1948*

# *Windmills in Brooklyn*

*PRUDENCIO DE PEREDA*

# *Windmills in Brooklyn*



NEW YORK *ATHENEUM* PUBLISHERS
*1960*

Library of Congress catalog card number 60-7774
Published simultaneously in Canada by
Longmans, Green & Company
Manufactured by Kingsport Press, Inc., Kingsport, Tennessee
Designed by Harry Ford
First Edition

TO JOHN AND ARLENE KOONS

*Like so much else in this book,* the title was contributed by my grandmother. She often criticized Grandfather for his lack of business sense and his otherworldliness, and once when she was doing this to a friend, the woman objected and defended my grandfather. "Don José is a man of great integrity," she said. "That is worth more, much more, than your business sense. He has ideals, like the great men of the world. He is like Quixote, like a true Don Quixote."

"Yes," Grandmother said, in her cold, biting way. "A true Don Quixote. Unfortunately for all of us, though, there are no windmills in Brooklyn."

"But one can suppose!" the friend said. "One can suppose!"

# *PART ONE*

# *Agapito*

# *Chapter One*

I THOUGHT when I was young that you worked according to your nationality. We were Spanish, and my father, grandfather and uncles were all in the cigar business. There was a definite rule about this, I believed—a *law*. I thought so particularly during those times that I listened to my father and the other men of our family talk business, and heard them complain bitterly about the cigar business and about what a dishonorable trade it was and how they were cursed the moment they took it up.

This used to surprise me—especially in regard to my father—because on the rare visits to his store it had seemed like a wonderful place. It had a broad, rich-looking, nickel-plated counter, neatly stacked with bright-colored boxes of cigars, and with shining hookahs and lighters standing along its top. The floor was white tile, and the inside wall of the store was a great mirror. The customers I'd seen had been well-dressed men with booming voices, rich gold chains around their full stomachs, and canes and gloves in their hands. There had been an air of wealth and strength in that store as I remembered it.

Still, my father was one of the most vehement in his denunciations of the cigar business. "Let them raise the blood to my face in shame," he once said, in his correct, intense Spanish, "if I permit any of my sons to go into this business! Yes. Let them do that!"

I admired my father for his ideas, but felt that he was just talking, that my three brothers and I were all fated for the cigar business just as my father and uncles had been. Indeed, even at this time my older brother, who was only ten but figured himself a wise American, had already begun to do some special errands for my father. He not only would deliver boxes of cigars to the hotels in the neighborhood of my father's store in the Boro Hall section of Brooklyn but would even take the elevated and go over the river and into the city to make deliveries.

When I begged him to tell me about this, he acted very casual and unafraid, and when, out of my genuine concern for him, I asked, "Aren't you going to be an aviator anymore?" he said, "Sure! What's the matter with you? What d'you think I'm saving my money for?" I pitied him all the more, and worried myself inside for him. He was doomed—just as my father and uncles had been doomed. He would never be an aviator—nor would I ever be a bullfighter; and poor Justo would never have his big shoeshine parlor or have his twin Bifanio as a sweeper. Bifanio hadn't made up his mind yet as to what he wanted to be, but the twins always did things together.

My older brother would never take me with him when he went on his errands. I was too young, though I was only two years younger than he. After we came home from school, he would put on his Sunday suit and new shoes and go down to my father's store on the trolley. Then he would take the el or even the subway to deliver the cigars. I often wept as I pleaded with him to take me—just once, just this once! I didn't want to get into the cigar business and was afraid of the city, but I would have risked anything to be allowed to ride on an elevated train. And I liked to go to my father's store anyway. It was located right in the center of the Spanish colony and it was nice to go there and see the Spanish men and get candy at the Spanish grocer's.

My brother never relented, and my first experience in the cigar business came through an accident and without his help. It was something bigger than had ever happened to him, and I should have felt boastful; instead, it filled me with terror and shame, and at once I understood the feelings of my father and the other men of our family.

How it happened was natural enough. Mother was making still another try to have a girl, a "little sister," as she explained formally to us, and we three younger boys were farmed out. My older brother Joe stayed at home because he could do errands, make phone calls and generally help around the house, and besides, as he explained to me, he was old enough to understand things. I didn't feel too bad, because I was going to Grandmother's and not to an aunt's, as the twins were. Going to Grandmother's had some responsibility, for there were always errands to be done and I would often have to act as translator. My grandmother spoke only about ten words of English, and my grandfather just a few more.

Grandfather and Grandmother didn't live in the Spanish colony now. They had moved to only a few blocks from us when we moved to a nicer section of

Brooklyn. Mother had said she wanted to be near a nice school for us boys, and she wanted a street without businesses. We owned our own house and were on a very nice street. Grandmother's place was on the ground floor of an apartment building, but the street they lived on was very pretty too.

On the third day of my stay there—it was the Fourth of July—Grandfather had announced early that he wouldn't "go out" today. "Going out" meant going to work. My grandfather was in the most stigmatized form of the cigar business—he was a *teveriano* or "junk dealer," one of those itinerant salesmen who were so scorned by the rest of the trade because they dealt completely in lies: in false labels, false representation of themselves and false merchandise—very cheap cigars for which they secured exorbitant prices—and so brought still more disgrace to the Spaniards who had enough as it was by merely being connected with the legitimate cigar business.

I had heard all this at home—listening eagerly because the *teveriano* was certainly the most interesting of all the cigar men—but I'd never been able to connect the fabulous stories of *teverianos* with my mild, sad grandfather. For one thing, he was always very poor.

Grandmother didn't turn to look at him as she answered, "Do you observe American holidays now?" She had a great dislike for everything American. She had been a great lady in Spain.

"One has to dance to the song they play," Grandfather said, shrugging his shoulders.

"And one has to pay the rent they ask!" Grandmother said very sharply. I knew I should have left the room then, but I felt too sorry for my grandfather. He was growing very red. "We're at the fourth now," Grandmother said. "That's five days late."

"I know that."

"Well?" Grandmother said, turning.

"I know that. I'm in accord with you. But not in front of the boy, please! Not in front of the boy, woman."

"The boy knows it!"

"But not from me!" Grandfather stood up suddenly and came over to me. His hands were trembling. He took my arm and led me into the front parlor. He stood me by the window and sat down in the big chair. "Watch the celebrations," he said. "Watch the celebrations!" I stared fixedly out the open window, knowing there weren't going to be any celebrations around here but not wanting to tell my grandfather.

We stayed there for only a short time, because the bell rang in a few moments—I couldn't see who it was—and quick, happy steps came up the stairs, and we heard Agapito's voice greeting my grandmother. He called her "Doña," the most respectful title in Spanish, but he was laughing and warm as he talked.

Just as Grandfather was not, Agapito was the perfect example of the *teveriano*. He was still a very young man and had only been in America a short time, but he was easily the most famous, as well as the most criticized, of the salesmen. He was dressed that day as I imagined a *teveriano* would dress: a fine white linen suit, brown patent-leather shoes with button tops, a bright polka-dot bow tie and a Panama straw hat with a multicolored band. When he came smiling into the front room, I thought he looked like the perfect man of the world, and he seemed to fill the room with brightness. He was very respectful to my grandfather, as he'd been to Grandmother, and when he suggested that they go out for a little bit he said it in a quiet, serious voice.

"We'll take the boy with us, yes?" he said, patting my shoulder and smiling at me. Agapito had neat, white teeth and a small black mustache. He had dark Spanish skin, and I thought he was very handsome. I'd always liked him, in spite of the stories I'd heard about him.

Grandfather answered Agapito's suggestion to go out by quietly shrugging his shoulders, but when Agapito suggested that they take me, his face took on the dark, stubborn look again.

"Yes, take the boy," my grandmother called from the kitchen. "He hasn't been out. He may see some things. Holiday things." My grandfather shrugged his shoulders again.

We took a trolley—an open summer trolley—and stayed on till the end of the line, and I saw that we'd come to the dock section. I could see the colored stacks of the big liners tied up at the piers. The big street was empty and quiet and that made the wonderful ships seem more intimate in the sun. Agapito kept pointing out things to me, but Grandfather walked along very quietly. He was dressed in his best black suit, with a black derby hat, and his face looked very worried. His drooping black mustache made his face look very sad.

When we'd gone a few blocks, we turned into a side street and went into a small cigar store. I saw that this was Miguelín's. I knew Miguelín from seeing him at home and at the Spanish dances. He was a little gray old man, and his store was dusty and old. He wrapped up seven new boxes of cigars for us, not wrapping them in brown paper, but just with a heavy string so that you could see it was cigars, and all the beautiful labels showed. Agapito gave him fourteen dollars. I counted them and figured out that it meant two dollars per box.

Grandfather wanted to pay, but Agapito stopped him and made him put his money away. Agapito seemed to have charge of everything—he'd paid our fares on the trolley too. He bent over and talked to Grandfather in a low voice while he patted him on the shoulder. I felt very happy about this. I wanted my grandfather to lose his worry.

When we left Miguelín's, we turned to the big street again and walked back the way we'd come. We walked very slowly, and Agapito kept talking to Grandfather and looking into each saloon that we passed. The saloons were the only places that were open today, and there weren't many men in any of them. We were coming to a big one on the opposite corner when Agapito said to my grandfather, "This one! This one seems good."

The saloon had a bright, shiny front and had a large hotel upstairs. I read the name "Monaghan" on the sign over the swinging doors. As we crossed, Agapito took my hand firmly, and as we went in I saw that the saloon was big and shiny and clean. It reminded me of my father's store. There was a long counter on one side with a great mirror on the wall, and another counter on the other side with trays of food filling it all along. The tile floor was very clean and had no sawdust on it, and there was a big back room with tables that had white tablecloths.

Agapito stood inside the doorway, smiling, looking around as if he liked the place. Then he led us over to the counter with the mirror. We found a place easily because there were only a few men standing there, and Agapito placed the cigar boxes on the counter and nodded and smiled to the man behind the counter. He pointed to my grandfather and then to himself and said, "Whiskey!" very plainly. He pronounced it "viskey." He patted me on the head and smiled at the man again and said, "Ginger ale!" He pronounced this well, except that he said "al" instead of "ale."

There was another man behind the counter, standing further back. He had his jacket off and his sleeves rolled up, but he didn't have an apron on. He was a big man with a red face, and he was smoking a big cigar. He had a gold chain across his vest and two big rings on his right hand, and he looked like one of my father's rich customers. When I stared at him, he winked at me and laughed. He'd been watching Agapito and my grandfather, who were leaning on the counter with their feet on the brass rail. Agapito had been talking in Spanish and laughing as he and my grandfather drank their whiskey.

The big man walked up to them slowly and patted the cigar boxes. Agapito turned his head suddenly, in surprise, and then smiled at the big man and bowed to him.

"Havanas?" the big man said. He had a strong, deep voice.

Agapito nodded quickly. "Yes! I am from Havana. I am from Havana."

"I mean the cigars," the big man said, laughing. He had brown teeth but a nice face.

"Oh! Also, also!" Agapito said. He laughed and kept nodding his head. "From Havana, also. For my friend. I bring them." He pointed outside. "The ship! You understand? From Havana to Spain. I bring them to friend here. I stop off." He spoke in short spurts, but he pronounced very clearly. He stopped smiling and became very serious as he pulled one of the boxes out of the bundle, opened it with his little gold knife and picked out two cigars carefully. He handed them over to the big man and nodded vigorously when the man seemed to hesitate. "For Fourth of July!" Agapito said. He smiled again. "Happy Fourth of July!" He nodded and pressed the cigars into the man's hand.

The big man smelled the cigars and nodded to Agapito. "Good flavor," he said. He turned and said something to the man in the apron and this man took the bottle and poured more whiskey into Agapito's and my grandfather's glasses. Agapito raised his glass to the big man, and then my grandfather did.

The big man kept smelling the cigars and then he patted the boxes again. "What would they cost?—How much?" he said, when Agapito looked puzzled. Agapito spread his hands. "For a friend," he said. "You understand. No . . ." He made the motion with his hands again.

"Customs?" the big man said.

"Customs!" Agapito nodded very quickly and smiled. He rubbed his hands. "No customs. No customs."

"Well, how much? How much, anyway?" The big

man patted the boxes. He had a strong big hand.

Agapito held a finger up, and turned to my grandfather. "This one seems to have money," he said in Spanish. "This one can pay."

"Take care, *hombre,*" my grandfather said.

"No, don't disquiet yourself, Don José. I know what I'm doing." Agapito patted Grandfather's arm, turned to the man and smiled. "My friend here," he said. "He remember. He remember everything." He ran his finger up and down the boxes. "All the boxes. Seven! Sixty dollars. Cost for my friend."

Sixty dollars! This was a shock to me: if a man buys seven boxes of cigars for fourteen dollars, two dollars per box, and sells them for—sixty dollars! I understood why the big man made such a face and then laughed. I hadn't minded all the lies that Agapito had told because I knew that *teverianos* worked like that, but when he asked this high, high figure I got shocked and embarrassed, and then very frightened for us. The glass felt heavy in my hand, and I held my head down because I knew that I was blushing. I'd heard that *teverianos* asked robber prices.

He was going to get us into trouble. He was making us take a chance—because he wanted to! And we were going to get into trouble.

The big man said something to Agapito, and then Agapito said, "Well—you know, sir. Havanas!"

I didn't hear the big man's answer, but then Agapito said very brightly, "You interested? You interested in cigars?" I hated his accent now. His lying.

"I was looking for ten boxes. I could use ten boxes," the big man said slowly.

Agapito was talking in Spanish then. He must

have been talking to my grandfather. "You stay here," he said, still speaking respectfully. "I will run to Miguelín's and get three more boxes. I will run fast. You stay here. This is a good thing."

"Yes, *hombre,* it is," I heard my grandfather say. "Let him take these seven boxes and let us be through here. Let it stay a good thing."

"There is no danger," Agapito said quickly.

"If there is, entrust it to me," my grandfather said sternly, and I looked up suddenly to see that his face had taken on the stubborn look again. "I wasn't thinking of that," he said. "I was thinking that we have a good thing. Let us take it, and be gone."

"I don't work like that," Agapito said. "You know that, Don José," he said more softly.

"Then, as you wish."

"You will stay?"

"As you wish."

I watched, fascinated, as Agapito turned back to smile at the big man who was leaning on the counter with his old cigar in his mouth. Agapito brought his hands together. "We fix it," he said, and nodded. "Three more boxes, I will bring from the boat. For ten boxes—" he ran his finger up and down the seven on the counter and held up three fingers—"ten boxes! For eighty dollars—for you!" He pointed at the big man.

The big man stared at Agapito for a moment, and then nodded and said, "Okay. Eighty dollars." What a fool this one is too, I thought. His face looked stupid to me now.

"You give me fifty dollars now," Agapito said. He smiled. "I give money to guard—small money—you understand? My friend wait here. I come back, with three more."

Did Grandfather understand that? Did Grandfather know what Agapito was saying? I stared at his face, but couldn't see anything. I was weak with fright and fear, but I didn't dare say a word. The big man had taken out his wallet without hesitation and given Agapito five new bills, tens they must have been. Agapito smiled and nodded as he put them in his wallet quickly. He patted Grandfather on the arm, saying, "Don't worry yourself. I'll be back immediately," and then patted me on the head—I couldn't duck fast enough—and went out into the street.

I stared at the floor. I wouldn't look at my grandfather. I'd finished the ginger ale, but I wouldn't go over to put the glass on the counter. I heard the big man say something to Grandfather that Grandfather didn't answer. "No speak English, eh?" the big man said, and laughed. He took up the bundle of cigars and moved down to the end of the counter, where I could see him by just lifting my eyes a little, and he began to open every box.

I had to look at my grandfather then. Did he see what danger we were in? He was staring at the mirror. His hands were steady, but he was sweating. I glared at him at first, but then I wanted to cry. I went up and put the glass by his side, and he looked down at me and then turned to stare up at the big man as he was opening each box. Then he turned back, finished his drink in one swallow and turned to me. His back was to the big man and he put his hand on my shoulder. I could smell the whiskey on his breath as he bent down. "Get thee out of here," he said. "Act as if thou art going calmly." My grandfather always used the familiar "thee" with us, and his voice was calm and easy now, but I could see that he was sweating badly. His hand felt very tight on my shoulder. "Get thyself to the trolley station. Stand by the trees there and wait for me. No matter how long, I will come. Do nothing but wait for me. I will escape this in some way. I will get out and get to thee. I will escape this and get to thee. In whatever way, I will.

"Without crying, thee!" he said. "Without crying!" I hadn't started to cry yet, but my lip had begun to tremble. I bit my lip and started to shake my head even before he'd finished. "And think well of me," he was saying. "Think well of me. I did not want this situation for thee. Thou wilt not? Thou wilt not do it?"

"No. I stay. I stay here with you."

His face had the stubborn look again and he pushed my shoulder but held his grip tightly on it. He glared at me, but I kept shaking my head. "Stay then!" he said. "Stay!" He dropped his hand from my shoulder but reached to take my hand, and then turned to lean on the bar again, holding my hand. A moment later, when he poured more whiskey into his glass, he did it with his left hand but poured it very neatly. He lifted the glass in his left hand and began to sip the whiskey slowly.

Grandfather had been a waiter in Spain. He was very proud of that. Then, just before he had come to the United States, he'd been a waiter at the best hotel in Tangier, Morocco; and a prince, a duke and two princesses had been among his patrons. My mother was born in Tangier, and though she couldn't remember anything of her part in the life there, she told us many stories about it. The three years spent in Tangier had been the happiest time in the life of her family.

My grandmother's brother had come to the United States some years before and made an immediate success as a *teveriano.* He wrote glowing letters to my grandmother, telling her of the wonderful opportunities in the trade and urging her to make José, my grandfather, see reason and come to America. Does he want to be a waiter all his life? the brother would ask. He'd felt very bad when she'd married a waiter. He was her only brother and they were very close.

Grandfather was content. He didn't want to leave. The letters got more boastful, and then pleading. Finally my granduncle sent enough money to pay first-class passage for all three, and the pressure was too much for my grandfather. He consented, and he came to the United States with his family—to a tenement district in Hoboken, New Jersey. They moved to Brooklyn shortly after, when my aunt was born, but to a tenement district again, and they had never lived better than that. Grandfather, as my mother would say in ending these stories, was just not a good salesman.

Seeing Grandfather pour the whiskey so neatly had made me think of what a wonderful waiter he'd been and of how he must feel about what he was doing now. I gripped his hand and stared up at him, and the anger I'd felt turned to pity. I love you, I thought. Once I pulled his arm and said, "We could go to the bathroom—first me, then you—and sneak out that way."

He glared down at me with a stubborn look. "No. In no such manner. When we go, we go through the front door. We are men." He turned to stare at the mirror, but then turned quickly back to me. "Dost thou have to go to the toilet? Truly?"

I shook my head.

"Good!" he said, and turned to the mirror.

I thought we stood like that for a long time—it seemed like a long, long time to me—but Agapito said later that he'd only been gone sixteen minutes, that he'd counted them. Agapito's face was sweating and he had his Panama hat pushed back on his head when he came in, but he was smiling and looked very happy, and his clothes were still very neat.

"I run! I run!" he said to the big man. "To ship. To ship and back!"

He'd put the new boxes on the counter and was opening each one with his penknife and holding the open box up to the big man. The boxes looked very new, and I thought that one of the labels looked wet. Surely the big man would see now. He would see the truth now, I thought. And it would serve Agapito right. He'd be in it now. Grandfather and I could run. We'd get away. Agapito was the one they would hold.

The big man smelled every box and even touched the wet wrapper, but he nodded seriously and then stupidly took out his wallet and gave Agapito three more ten-dollar bills. The man with the apron had filled Agapito's glass again and Agapito held out one of the bills to him, but he shook his head. Then Agapito put the bills in his wallet and picked out a one-dollar bill that he folded and handed to the man in the apron. "For you," he said. "For you." He smiled and nodded. Then he held up the whiskey, smiled and nodded again and drank it in one gulp.

I had been tugging at Grandfather's hand, wanting to start, wanting us to go, but Grandfather held his tight grip and waited until Agapito had shaken hands with both men; then he himself nodded to them and we all turned toward the door.

We walked very slowly as we went outside and crossed the street. Grandfather wanted to walk fast, but Agapito was holding his arm and walking very slowly. "Don't worry yourself," he said, after a moment. "We'll turn down the first street. For now, we walk slowly—very slowly, and with dignity."

We turned down the first street, walked down that block and then turned in the direction of the trolleys. As soon as we'd made this last turn, Agapito stopped and took out his wallet. He handed Grandfather four ten-dollar bills. Grandfather pushed them back. *"Hombre!"* he said. "Don't embarrass me."

"Please!" Agapito said. "This is your share."

"It's too much."

"It's half. We were equally involved." Agapito pressed the bills into Grandfather's hand. "Equally!" he said, letting go.

Grandfather put the bills in his little black purse. "I'm very appreciative. Very," he said.

"For nothing!" Agapito said. "For nothing!" As we walked now, he was smiling and happy again. He took off his Panama hat and rubbed his face with a big silk handkerchief. "One has to see these things,

Don José! One has to see them. To believe them, one has to see them. Havanas!" He shook his head and laughed. "And you mustn't feel that we cheat them!" he said, when Grandfather didn't answer. "This one buys them as Havanas. He gives them out as Havanas—probably at some festival—and those who take them, take them as Havanas—and smoke them! No matter how bad the cigars, for them they are Havanas. Yes, Don José! We sell Havanas, they buy Havanas."

On the trolley, after he'd paid our fares, Agapito slipped a half dollar into the conductor's pocket. "For Fourth of July," he said. The conductor blushed, and nodded. Later, Agapito stood up and took off his hat. "Life for the United States of America!" he called out. "Happy Fourth of July to everybody!" The two people who were sitting up at the front end of the trolley smiled and shook their heads. They thought he was drunk.

Agapito left soon after we got home. Then Grandmother went out. "I'll get some ham," she said. "We'll eat well, tonight." Grandfather and I were in the front room, and she had come to the door. "The delicatessen has good ham."

Grandfather nodded. "We're most fortunate," he said, without looking up. "Most fortunate."

Grandmother turned back and stared at him with a cold face. She was dressed in her black skirt and black silk waist, and she looked like the pictures of the Queen Mother in the Spanish magazines we had, except that Grandmother was much more beautiful. "Yes," she said, in a calm voice. "Most fortunate.

You, in particular. You needn't go out for some days, now. Perhaps you can grow a beard, here."

Grandfather got very red, but didn't look up. He shrugged his shoulders as Grandmother turned and went out. After a moment he reached over to me and pulled me to the side of the chair. He kept his arm around me and patted my head. "Thou!" he said. He looked straight at me. "Thou must forget what thou heard today, what thou sawst. All of it! Forget especially what thy grandmother said. She is a fine woman. Nothing of today was like her. It is I who am weak. The fault is mine. Thou wilt understand this some day. Thou wilt, yes. What thou must remember is this—" he pressed my shoulder—"that thou must be strong. Remember that! Let no woman —whether she be thy mother who is my own flesh, or the woman thou wilt marry—let none of them press thee or influence thee in choosing thy profession. Thou—thou alone—must move through the world to make thy money. Thou alone must suffer —so thou must choose. And hold to that! Thou art the bullfighter, no?"

"Or one who guides an elevated train," I said. "One of those."

"Good. Thou might change, but whatever thou shouldst choose, hold to it. Grip it well!"

I nodded.

"Dost thou know what she referred to in that of the beard?" he said in a softer voice.

"No, Grandfather," I lied.

"Well, it was this: I had a fine beard when I was a waiter in Tangier. It was a full, well-cut beard, and I was a fine figure with it. One afternoon, the major-domo, Don Felix, came to me and said, 'José, you must shave that beard. Too many patrons are coming in and talking to you and treating you as the major-domo. I regret this, but you must shave it, because there is only one major-domo here, and it is me. No one else can look like a major-domo. No one else will.'

"I went home to thy grandmother and told her this, and she said, 'Yes. The man has reason. You must shave your beard.' I had thought that she would have objections, that she would show anger. I had thought that she loved the beard as I did—it was a fine beard. But she did not; or, if she did, she would not let this stand before Don Felix's objection.

"So, I cut it off!" my grandfather said. He brushed his hand under his chin. "That was a mistake. I should have held to my first thought. I should have defended myself. I should have left my place and sought another—in Tangier, or Gibraltar, or La Linea, where there are fine hotels. *I* was doing the waiting, and *I* should have thought of *myself*." He stopped and stared at me. "Thou seest?" he said. "Stop thou at the first mistake. Stop there!"

I nodded, and he pressed my shoulder again and then reached over and lifted me onto his lap. He cradled my head on his shoulder and rocked slowly back and forth. "We must gladden ourselves," he said, "before she comes. We must gladden ourselves and be smiling. This is difficult for her, too. Difficult! We must gladden ourselves now. Yes. We must gladden ourselves for her."

I was nodding my head to say, Yes, when my forehead felt something wet, and I looked up and saw that the tears were falling down his cheeks.

# *Chapter Two*

As long as I can remember, Agapito Lopez was the most popular man in the Spanish colony, but there were only two people who really liked him—Grandmother and me. The others made a fuss over Agapito wherever he went; people would laugh and talk and drink with him, and pat him on the back, but afterwards they would tell the most horrible stories about him. They would talk about his character, about the way he worked and about how he was giving a bad name to every Spaniard in America. "Don't lend a bit of attention to those stories," Grandmother said when I asked her about them. "Those people are jealous of Agapito. They envy him. They abuse him to keep their pride—the little they have."

"The stories aren't true?" I said.

"They're exaggerations," Grandmother said. "They can be big lies, exaggerations."

"I know Agapito can do terrible things," I said. I was thinking of the time I had gone out selling with him and Grandfather, and of how he had embarrassed Grandfather with his lying and his cheating. "I remember one time—"

"Yes. You remember the time you went out with him and your grandfather," she interrupted me, "and was due there early, and he would advise Doña Felisa of Agapito's coming. Agapito accepted happily.

"You can imagine!" he said to me. "That was just what I wanted—to meet important people—and here it was happening to me on my first day in America. This gentleman who spoke to me was Don Mariano Benitez. He was one of the great *teverianos,* you know. And when I got to your grandmother's I met many other important people—the most important, of course, your grandmother!" Agapito held up his finger in that definite gesture. "Yes! That was the fortunate thing for me—meeting your grandmother. The Saint! Don't smile," he said. "I know how you feel about religion, but for me, she will always be La Santa. And how wise she was!" He put his finger to his eye. "How she could see inside. Let me tell you."

Agapito had promised his father and stepmother that he would do nothing wicked in America, that he would use no tricks or wiles of the big city to earn money, but when he heard of *teverianos* on the ship he had become immediately intrigued with them. He felt sure that he could do well as one of these fancy, cheating cigar salesmen. He remembered his promise to his parents, reluctantly, but he played with the idea because America and *teverianos* were still some distance away. Meanwhile he hoped for a sign.

At Grandmother's, he talked a good deal to Don Mariano about *teverianos* and, much to Agapito's delight, the great man offered to take him on as an apprentice. Later my granduncle Don Isidro, who was also a well-known *teveriano,* made him the same offer. "I was very bright, you see," Agapito explained to me. "I'm an old man, now—" he wasn't, of course, and he would never have seemed old to me, anyway —"but, in those days, I was young and very bright. I had no education, but I was bright—and brave. You know, maybe too brave for my own good. That's why they did that. That's why these men were impressed with me." He was ecstatic over these offers but, of course, could not accept them immediately. He was waiting for a sign.

Agapito stayed very late at Grandmother's. He was so happy that he did not want to leave, and he stayed until the last. When they were alone Grandfather advised Agapito against becoming a *teveriano*. He himself was one, and was miserable. He advised Agapito not to be tempted by the hope of sudden monies, that there were many dangers in being a *teveriano*. But Grandmother said, Yes, he should become one. She could see that he was young and willing, she said, that he had courage. That was the most important thing, to be daring. If he felt like being a *teveriano,* he should get into it and resolve to be daring—to try it to the full. That was the only way to do it. That was the only way to win as a *teveriano*.

"Don't push the boy," Grandfather said.

"I'm not pushing him," Grandmother said. "I can see how much he wants to be one, and I think he'll be a good *teveriano,* a real one."

"She seemed to see inside me," Agapito told me. "Truly yes! How wise this saint was! She seemed to know how eager I was to be a *teveriano,* how anxious I was to have the word from her. And she gave it, she gave it to me. That was my sign—her word. This saint—who seemed to be speaking for my dead mother—told me Yes, go—become a *teveriano;* you have our word. You have our consent."

Agapito, of course, was too interested to see the bitterness in Grandmother's advice. I'm sure that she meant what she told him, but she must have given this advice to Agapito with a bitter feeling. I wondered how Grandfather felt as she talked. Anyway, she was right about Agapito. That was good advice.

He became an apprentice to Don Mariano the next week. Before that, however, Grandmother helped him get into a good boarding house. Like most immigrants, Agapito had first taken a room in New York near the docks, but now he went into one of the big, clean Spanish boarding houses in Brooklyn Heights, in the heart of the Spanish colony.

There were four of these boarding houses when I was young and after we had moved out of the colony, we children used to love to go to visit them with my father or grandfather. The visits were on Sunday afternoons and we always stayed for the evening meal of *paella.* I knew that the adults had to pay for these meals, but I didn't mind because Father always seemed rich to me and I knew that, if Grandfather went, my mother would give him the money beforehand for all of us.

Agapito went to Don Jacobo's house which I always thought was the best because it had the biggest dining room, and while he was telling me the story of being there I could remember the rare wonderful meals we had in that dining room. The regular boarders sat at a big table in the center while we and the other guests sat at tables for four and six placed around the walls. There wasn't much distance between any two of the tables and conversation went all around very easily while the adults drank their *aperitifs,* and then Don Jacobo, his wife and daughter would bring in the steaming, covered casseroles of pungent *paella.* It was usually made of chicken and rice, with peppers and Spanish sausage, but sometimes there were shrimps added. It was called *paella a la valenciana* then. Father or Grandfather would serve us our first portions and, later, we were allowed to serve ourselves seconds from the still steaming casserole.

*Paella* is the national dish of Spain but we had it only rarely at home. Mother didn't have the time to make it, and Grandmother couldn't afford to. So these times at the boarding houses were very special.

My father and all of my uncles had lived at a boarding house in Brooklyn Heights until they were married and they liked to go back to eat *paella* or to play cards. Grandfather had never lived in a boarding house, but he enjoyed going back to visit with his friends. I always tried to get invited whenever I could because I liked to be among Spaniards and listen to them talk. There were more Spaniards in Brooklyn Heights than in any other place I knew, and I didn't feel like a foreigner there, the way I did in my neighborhood or at school.

We rarely saw Agapito at his boarding house on these Sunday visits, and I heard that he wasn't around there much. I knew the real reason for this—Agapito never played cards and he wasn't too interested in food—but it was the beginning of some

Spaniards' dislike for him. They thought he was a snob; he had no time for his own people.

As a young apprentice to Don Mariano, Agapito accompanied him on his rounds—which sometimes went as far west as Chicago—carried the boxes of cigars and did other menial chores, watched and listened, and received one fourth of the profits from which his own expenses had already been deducted.

An apprentice usually stays for a year, or sometimes two, but the relationship between Don Mariano and Agapito lasted only four months. They parted in a friendly way, with Don Mariano saying that he thought Agapito had seen everything he could teach him.

I had heard Don Mariano tell this part of the story many years before and now I remembered him saying, "Yes. That was the truth. I had taught him everything I knew. I was afraid that he was going to teach me everything he knew."



Don Mariano was a dignified old man with a deep bass voice and a shining bald dome. He was heavy but he walked erect. He had a florid face and his bright vivid eyes seemed to see very deeply. As children, we liked him very much because he often gave us half dollars and was always ready to talk to us. He seemed a very nice old man, even though we knew he had some kind of bad reputation. Don Mariano wasn't being mean in telling these stories about Agapito—he had a certain pride in "his apprentice" and most of the jokes in the stories were on him, Don Mariano.

Agapito was telling me now that the first big call he had made as Don Mariano's apprentice had been to the rectory of Saint Patrick's Cathedral. Don Mariano often called there to sell cigars, and was known to the Monsignor who handled such matters. He charged his usually exorbitant prices for the cigars because Don Mariano, like most of the Spanish men in the colony, was an anticlerical, but he always conducted his calls to the Saint Patrick rectory with unusual dignity and care. He made a point of stressing this to Agapito, and Agapito nodded and then watched everything very carefully during the call.

Then, as soon as they were safely outside, Agapito had asked permission to make a suggestion. Of course, Don Mariano said. Well, they were acting too cautiously, Agapito thought. He respected Don Mariano's methods very much—he could see by the profits how effective they were—but certainly, in this case of the Cathedral, they were acting with too much caution. After all, they started as fakes—they went in under a false impression—so why not carry this a little further?

And how was that? Don Mariano asked curtly.

"Let us go as priests," Agapito said.

"As priests?"

"Yes," Agapito said. He knew that this idea must be surprising to Don Mariano but allow him to explain. In the first place, it would take only collars and shirts to add, since they already had black suits. He would think up an appropriate story and verify every needed point, and then coach Don Mariano for the telling of it. Of course he knew they couldn't go back to the Cathedral like that after so short a time, but he'd noticed some very fine churches in Brooklyn where there must be much money in the parishes.

Don Mariano pointed out that using disguises was a very dangerous thing. Posing as someone by mouth—a Cuban just off the ship, for example—was an almost innocent thing and not very far from the truth, but wearing a disguise of any kind might bring in the law. He had never had any trouble with the law, Don Mariano said, and he had been a *teveriano* for twenty-five years.

There was another thing wrong with this, Don Mariano pointed out. If they posed as priests to priests, one of the real priests might discover the trick and then it would be all around the country—everybody knew what an organization those fellows had—and the church would be lost to the *teverianos.* And it was one of their best customers.

In spite of this, however, Don Mariano finally consented to go along with Agapito. When he told the story himself, he said he felt he had a protective responsibility toward the boy and he wanted to be certain that Agapito didn't get into any real trouble. This might be a fiasco, Don Mariano thought, and he wanted to be at the boy's side in case of trouble. It was a matter of pride.

Agapito, though, had no such fears. He arranged everything. He'd been in America less than two weeks, and he could not have known more than twenty words of English, but he discovered where to buy the ecclesiastical collars and shirts—in Barclay Street, New York—and found out the residence of the Bishop of Brooklyn, which he figured would be the richest parish house in Brooklyn.

He coached Don Mariano in the story he was to tell—it was a pretty logical story, Don Mariano thought—and, about a week after the visit to Saint Patrick's, they made their call on the richest parish house in Brooklyn, dressed in their ecclesiastical clothes and carrying twelve boxes of cigars.

Again, they spoke to a Monsignor. "In this country, the Monsignors are like sergeants in an Army," Don Mariano had said. "In our country, they have dignity and position. Here, they do the rough work."

Don Mariano introduced Agapito and himself as two Spanish priests on their way back to Spain from Cuba. When the boat docked here in Brooklyn, they had decided to pay their respects to the Bishop. They had heard of him in Spain—very much—and they wanted to call on him.

The Bishop was busy, the Monsignor said. Very busy, he was sorry to say.

"Well, no matter," Don Mariano said—he felt secretly glad that they would not have to deal with the Bishop, this fellow was bad enough—no matter, he still would like to leave these for the Bishop, and he ceremoniously handed over two boxes of cigars. "As a sign of respect," he said, translating the Spanish expression literally. "Our respect for the Bishop."

"Thank you," said the Monsignor. "Thank you!" He looked surprised and smiled at them for the first time.

"I could see that this one must have been hit by *teverianos* before," Don Mariano said, "and my giving him the boxes surprised him, surprised him very much." Don Mariano took advantage of this change of feeling to explain how two Spanish priests happened to have such a big supply of excellent Havana cigars. "The Monsignor could see," he said, "just by smelling the tobacco, these were pure Havanas."

Well, this is how it was: they were two priests from northern Spain—Agapito nudged him at this point. When he turned to him, Agapito smiled at him and nodded toward the Monsignor and said, "Our names. The names!" in Spanish. Don Mariano smiled slowly and turned back to the Monsignor. "Oh, yes," he said. "You don't know our names." He would have preferred to keep it like that, but he said them in a softer voice to the Monsignor and hoped that he didn't understand them at all. Actually they were the names of two priests from Agapito's village, and Agapito explained that this was an important note because it lent frankness to the story right at the beginning.

As the Monsignor knew, Don Mariano went on quickly, there were many men from their part of Spain in Cuba, and their Bishop liked to send priests there whenever he could, to see to it that these Spanish people were still practicing their true Catholic faith. He couldn't do this often—as the Monsignor could understand—because it was so expensive, but he did it as much as possible, and he always liked to send an older and a younger man.

Well, after they had finished their mission, their good sons in Cuba wanted to show their appreciation. They wanted to give them a gift. But the Monsignor knew how poor they were—they were just ordinary workers, working in the huge cigar factories there. So they had given their priests the most valuable gifts they knew of—pure Havana cigars. "You see, they know about the prices that these bring," Don Mariano said. "They know through their unions." And so they had given the priests these cigars.

Of course he and his companion had accepted the

gifts with voluble pleasure, Don Mariano went on. What else could they do? But the Monsignor would understand—what would two poor priests do with such expensive cigars? It would be immoral to smoke them—especially since their church needed so much. There was an altar cloth, for example, that his young friend had been trying to buy for two years now. The Monsignor would understand all these things, of course. So they had decided to sell the cigars for their churches. They had hoped that the Bishop could advise them.

"How much are they?" the Monsignor wanted to know, nodding toward the other ten boxes. He had been listening very seriously, but he said this quickly and surely.

Oh, they couldn't think of selling the cigars to the Bishop or to anyone here, Don Mariano told him. They were so expensive.

"Well, how much?"

Don Mariano stared at the ten boxes and seemed to figure. He saw how closely the Monsignor was watching him, and he told us he felt that Agapito was waiting even more tensely. "I was, *niño,*" Agapito said now. "This was very important to me. It was my first try." They had agreed before on two possible prices, and Agapito sighed as Don Mariano gave the bigger price—Agapito's suggestion. "One hundred and fifty dollars," Don Mariano said. "You see how expensive they are. The Bishop could not possibly . . ."

"It is expensive," the Monsignor said. "Yes. Too expensive for us, of course, but . . ." He looked at Don Mariano and then at the cigars as he thought.

"Of course, we know people who could use cigars, and since you've been so kind to us. . . . Would they pay for the altar cloth?" he said very seriously.

"Yes," said Don Mariano. "With the money we already have. The money collected from our poor people—you know how poor the people of Spain are. The cloth is being made in Madrid by women sewers —women who are artists."

The Monsignor nodded. Yes, yes, he knew. He thought for a moment more, and then said, "Excuse me, I'll be right back."

While they were alone, Don Mariano and Agapito did not talk. Don Mariano said he had his own private thoughts about what the Monsignor might be doing, but he was too proud to mention them. Agapito got up and looked over the room and the bookshelves. He was trying to act, he told me now, as a young, intelligent priest should act, but Don Mariano said he looked like somebody who was thinking of buying the place. When the Monsignor came back he had a name and address written on a paper for them. It was the name of an alderman friend, the Monsignor told them, and he could use the cigars for a political dinner he was giving the next afternoon. The Monsignor gave them careful directions about getting to the alderman's office, and thanked them for the cigars they'd given the Bishop. "Remember us in your prayers," was the last thing he said, and Don Mariano confessed that he felt his neck and blushed. Agapito, however, only smiled and nodded effusively.

On their way to the alderman's office Don Mariano's doubts increased, but his pride prevented his saying anything. Agapito kept encouraging him and telling him not to worry. Don Mariano said he wasn't worried; he just didn't like the idea of going to jail. Well, they could always run, Agapito said. "Can you imagine?" Don Mariano said to us. "Me, run? Not so much for the bad heart—but can you imagine me running?" He was a heavy, florid-faced man and very dignified. "I never run," he said to Agapito. "Never."

"Of course I was more frightened than the old man," Agapito said to me now. "That's why I was talking to him so. I wanted him to stay strong; I got him angry, but you know what happened next."

Don Mariano's pride was so hurt that when they got to the alderman's office he raised the price of the cigars. He was scared, but he felt real pleasure at seeing Agapito's surprise and shock. The alderman, too, was shocked. He was a stocky, sad-faced Irishman and he had pulled back as Don Mariano told him the price of the cigars—one hundred and seventy-five dollars. "Whew!" he said, but shook his head sternly when Don Mariano started to explain about the need for the altar cloth. "No, that's okay, Father," he said. "Monsignor Byrnes told me. He told me all about it." He had taken a roll of bills out of his pocket as he talked, but now he excused himself for a moment and went into another office. He came back with the one hundred and seventy-five dollars—three fifty-dollar bills, one twenty and one five. Don Mariano thanked him.

"I hope they're good Havanas, Father," the alderman said.

"They are," Don Mariano said.

"Yes," Agapito said. He nodded, smiling. "We may be back—tell him," he said to Don Mariano in Spanish. "My friend wishes to thank you as well," he said to the alderman.

When they were out on the street, Agapito shook Don Mariano by the hand. "Do you see?" he said, happily. "Do you see? There's money there—in the church. Didn't I tell you? Didn't I tell you?"

"Yes," Don Mariano said. "But they can keep it as far as I'm concerned. I don't like this. I don't like the disguises and the politicians."

They put on the disguises just once more. That was on a trip to Baltimore, and Don Mariano figured that they were far enough from New York to risk it. Their story was that their boat was at Philadelphia, but they'd made the trip to Baltimore to see the "famous" cathedral there and to call on the Archbishop. This time they actually made the sale at the church, and afterwards Don Mariano told Agapito it was the last time he would put on a disguise. He felt he had proved to Agapito that he was willing to try—but the risk was too great, he said. It wasn't worth it for him—he hoped Agapito would feel the same way.

"Very well," Agapito had said. "All right." He hadn't realized, he said, that Don Mariano had such a conscience about the church. He had thought——

"Conscience, nothing!" Don Mariano said. He had no conscience about the church—he just had respect for their organization. Putting on a disguise was bad enough, but when you dealt with these fellows you had to keep a very sharp eye ready. What happens to a priest in Brooklyn, a priest in Chicago will know the next day. They had a system and an organization, and he wasn't going to risk fooling with them any more.

"And I advised him not to risk it," Don Mariano told us. "I know he did it a few times more, though, in spite of my advice, and he'll probably keep doing it until they spot him. Then, when they turn him over to the Irish cops . . ." He shook his head sadly.

"But I only did it twice more," Agapito told me now. "And I stopped it for a very simple reason—nothing like fear of cops, or anything like that; nothing like a conscience of the church. It was a very simple reason. I couldn't tell it to Don Mariano, of course. I couldn't tell it to anyone—because I knew they wouldn't believe me. I'll tell it to you, *hijo*. Let me tell it to you."

He told me that the next time he'd put on a disguise to take cigars to a church, he'd used a cassock. This was a more complete disguise but it had a more familiar look, Agapito thought. He wanted to feel more like a priest, he said. The time was just a little while after he'd left Don Mariano, and the first place he tried, of course, was Saint Patrick's. He'd bought a good second-hand cassock in Barclay Street and he wore a light topcoat over it—to give it the look of a visiting priest who was just taking a quick half hour or so off the boat. There was a different priest in the rectory this time, but Agapito wasn't too worried about this, because the last visit was months back and he had since grown a mustache. "And, of course, I could talk English now—much more." He felt like a different person—and so he imagined he must look like one. He had only five boxes of cigars but, as before, the price was exorbitant and, of course, his story was different.

"I told them my story honestly," he said. "I didn't lie to create pity or anything like that. I just told them practically. I was a poor priest from Cuba. I had to come to New York—or Philadelphia—to purchase some medicines for my clinic, a clinic for the very poor. The captain of the ship was a good friend of mine and he let me make the trip third class at half price. I would say Mass, or do any religious service necessary. Of course I would eat in first class, once a day—to have a good meal, you know. I brought the cigars with me for the straight purpose of selling them. I knew they were good Havanas—some of my parishioners worked in the best factories and they would steal a few from time to time and give them to me and I would put them in boxes to sell here. I told them the straight, true story," Agapito said sincerely. "I had to make a good profit on the cigars and that was all."

He did very well. He tried it the next day in Philadelphia, and then he stopped it forever because of what happened two days later in Brooklyn. He had tried the second richest Catholic church in Brooklyn one night and done very well, and, since it was still early and he was feeling lucky and successful, he had gone back to the little cigar store and gotten three more boxes. He stopped at the first Catholic church he came to on the way from the store. It was in the waterfront area in Brooklyn, Agapito said, but it was a huge church and it looked certain to have some money. The church had big grounds around it, too, and the rectory was set well back. "What a surprise that was for me, when I got in," Agapito said.

First of all, there was no housekeeper. The priest himself opened the door; the rectory was dilapitated and dusty. This priest was the pastor and the only priest of the church. He told Agapito this as they were sitting down.

His appearance touched Agapito immediately. He was a thin, gray man, and the sleeves of his cassock were frayed. The garment itself was discolored with age. Agapito took out some cigars immediately and gave them to the priest. He began to smoke one with great enjoyment. It was a long time since he'd been able to afford these, he told Agapito. He brought out a bottle of domestic sherry. "It was so old it was almost vinegar," Agapito said.

Of course, the priest told him, he just couldn't even think of buying the cigars. He couldn't afford it, but he offered Agapito three dollars for his clinic. He wished he had more, he said.

Agapito gave him the cigars. The priest protested very much, but Agapito explained that he had sold well to other churches, and that his clinic could afford this little setback. The next day he had his cassock cleaned and pressed, and sent it anonymously to the priest. It was in excellent condition—much better than the priest's own—and the two men were about the same size.

"I couldn't get over the shock of seeing this man so poor—in such a rich organization as the Church. I honored that man—I knew he believed in Christ—and I knew I couldn't pose as a priest again. I would always be thinking of him. So I gave it up. Let the church keep its injustice, I thought—I didn't want to be a part of it. I was very young, and I wanted to feel happy. Besides, I knew it would be a little dangerous to go to too many churches in the east here, and so I felt I ought to stop it now. Let the Church be for women and children, I thought—as it is in Spain. I stopped treating with it then, and I have stayed that way. Of course," he quickly added, "if it should ever come to pass that you need something from the Church, some reference or something like that, just come to me, *niño*. I will arrange it for you. I know you have nothing to do with the Church, but if you should ever need something from them, come to me. I have many friends in the Church—authorities!—and I will fix it for you."

Agapito used to make the offer of help to me very often. It was the way he ended most of the stories he told me and, at first, I used to think he was just being polite. I found out later, though, that he actually meant it, but that was many years after this and it had nothing to do with the Church. . . .

I should have been surprised at these stories of Agapito and the priests, and I should have been shocked when I'd heard them first from Don Mariano. I was a very sincere, believing Catholic at that time but, even as a boy, I understood that Spanish men did not have to be Catholics—only women did.

Grandfather, Father and my uncles never went to church; in fact, they talked against it. Grandfather didn't talk as much as the others, or ever make fun of the Church, but he never urged us to go to Mass.

It was Mother and Grandmother who made us go to Mass every Sunday, and Mother sent us to parochial school. My aunts did the same with my cousins, and we children were all made to feel that we were strict Catholics. Grandmother, Mother and the aunts did not go to church themselves, but they told us that they didn't have the time, and would be glad to go if only they could.

My older brother Joe and my cousin Eduardo said that they would stop going to Mass as soon as they were old enough to wear long pants. Men didn't have to go to church, they said. They implied that you lost the necessity of going to Mass through growing up. Secretly I envied this feeling in them, but I was too afraid of the Church and of hell ever to stop thinking of going to Mass myself. In fact, I believed so sincerely that I thought I would have to keep on going in order to pray for Grandfather's and Father's souls and the souls of all the men in the Spanish colony who had lost their religion.

When I hinted at this, Joe and Ed merely sneered at me and said that I was just a sissy, but, in the end, it was I who was the first to stop going to Mass. I was going to college at the time—the only one of our generation to go—and Joe and Ed changed their tune. Now they criticized me for losing my religion and said that I was being ruined by too much education. They had not wanted to go to college themselves, and had even quit high school to get jobs.

Mother and the aunts were also angry when I stopped going to Mass. They said a college education was no good if it made me lose my religion. My father and uncles approved, however; ironically enough, it was only Agapito, of the men, who chided me. "Spaniards have always been Catholic, *niño,"* he said. "We men have been corrupted by the money of this country—that's the bad thing! Don't let this happen to you. Spain will always be Catholic—in spite of all the Anarchists. Don't ever doubt that! And you are always a Spaniard."

# Chapter Three

AGAPITO LOPEZ was born in a little *pueblo* in Galicia, the province that sits in the northeast corner of Spain, above Portugal. Unlike most of Spain, Galicia is green and fertile, but the little peasant-farmers whose houses clutter into a *pueblo* and who have small fields scattered over the land and hillside are only a little better off than the peasants on the arid plains of Spain. Agapito was the oldest of a family of three brothers and one sister and, when his father remarried after his mother's death, three more children were added to the family. Being the oldest son, Agapito stood first in line for the best of his father's lands, but ever since he could remember he was determined to leave Spain as soon as he came of age—or, more importantly, as soon as he got the money.

Agapito hated the hard work and the bare living of the Spanish farmer, but the life he had seen in the cities was just as harsh. What depressed Agapito most about Spain was the lack of reward in any place for intelligence or sharpness. Even in the Army or the Church, the young men of the lower classes never got anywhere. In Agapito's time—the 1890s—many men that he'd heard of, and some that he'd actually seen, had gone to Cuba, Mexico or Argentina to make their fortunes. After ten or fifteen years some of them would return to Spain as rich *"Americanos."* Agapito was determined, though, to go to the United States, to New York in particular, where there was more money and where it could be made faster. Agapito had always heard New York referred to as a wicked city, full of snares for the innocent and the honest, but he was certain he could cope with these.

He was a disciplined young man and calmly avoided the usual traps of the *pueblos'* young men. He would not take a field from his father as a gift when he was sixteen—and then have to work like a slave to buy seed to keep it going. He avoided military service by developing pains in his chest and back, and while the other young men of his age were taking their girls for long walks on the first warm evenings, Agapito relieved his tensions with a plump widow in the next *pueblo.* He had a girl, of course, among the ones of his own age in the *pueblo,* but he wanted to move very warily there. Fortunately again for him she was a quiet, shy and patient girl.

Agapito had gone into the affair with the widow with simple intentions and, as he said, "no dreams," but it was one of the most rewarding things he'd ever done. When she died suddenly during the third winter of their affair, she left him the magnificent sum of seventy-five dollars. He was surprised and delighted and wanted to leave for "Cuba" immediately, but his father promised him that if Agapito would see him through another season, he would give him twenty-five dollars more. Agapito agreed—this new money would serve to buy him a good suit. The following October, Agapito left for New York—saying he was going to Havana.

For a long time Agapito wrote home as if he were actually in Havana, knowing that his father would construe the United States stamp on the letters as just another indication of *Yanqui* power, but he did tell the truth about his being a cigar salesman—an honest one, of course—and about the wonderful friends he had made. Almost immediately he began to send presents—useful things like clothes for his brothers and sisters and farm tools for his father. He also wrote faithfully to his girl, and soon he began to send her small sums of money to be saved for her trousseau and their home.

Agapito never lost these connections with Spain. As his prosperity increased he intensified them, and that was true for the rest of his life. He moved closer to Spain and his people there as he made more money and grew more successful here. This was a part of him I could not understand at first, because it was just the opposite of the usual *teveriano* way. All *teverianos* talked about going back to Spain—if only to die there, as some of the older ones said—but they rarely did. By the time they had made their fortunes, their children, who had all been born here, were happy Americans, their own parents in Spain had died and their brothers and sisters had stopped writing from there. They still considered themselves Spaniards—they spoke little English and never thought of themselves as Americans—but they were bound now by an American life and they felt reluctant to follow a dream alone.

If they went on a visit to Spain, they came back very quickly and never went again. Two of the older *teverianos,* of Don Mariano's generation, actually went back to Spain to die—they were both very ill and their families knew they would never come back—but the rest of the *teverianos* are buried in Brooklyn or in the new cemeteries in Queens.

The big difference with Agapito was that he knew he would go back to Spain. He *acted* as if he would from the very beginning. As soon as he had sufficient funds—it was only two years after he had come to New York—he went back to Spain on a visit, married his girl and bought two acres of land from his father. They were craggy and stone-filled and on a hillside, and no use to his father as farm land, but Agapito planned to build a house there later—"the best house in the province." He had to rush back to New York, of course, and he left his bride in care of her mother. A simple peasant girl might not immediately understand the way Agapito earned his fabulous money, and Agapito rightly thought that it was too early to explain to her.

He went back for the birth of his first son, and this pattern was repeated over seven years and five children. Agapito was criticized in the Spanish colony for this cold-blooded treatment of his wife and children. The poor, captive woman stayed in the little *pueblo* bearing children, it was said, while Agapito gallivanted around the United States making his deals and cavorting with other women. There were always three or four members of the colony who swore that they had once seen Agapito with a "painted" woman during these years. My Aunt Elvira did meet Agapito on the subway one afternoon with a strange woman but, rather than run away, Agapito had introduced her very pleasantly and courteously and had invited my aunt to have dinner with them. "He said she was the wife of his cousin in Cuba," Aunt Elvira told us, "but I don't know. She was always calling him 'Pito.' "

"And what do you call him?" my grandmother asked her.

"Well, 'Pito,' too," my aunt said, "but . . ."

"There are no *buts,*" Grandmother said. "Stop it there."

I was too young to understand the stories of the women at the time and later they didn't seem too important, because Agapito's affairs never had the results of some of the other *teverianos'*—a late "sickness," that was usually syphilis or illegitimate children quietly brought into the lives of the fathers when the children were twelve or fourteen. As far as the other stories were concerned—the treatment of Agapito's wife and children—I could never believe them. When I saw Agapito with his children later, I had never seen a warmer family. There was a real feeling between his sons and him and, since I had missed that myself, I envied them. His wife was a sad woman, but that could easily have been due to what happened in New York after the family finally came to this country for good.

At this time of my life I could understand Agapito's intention of going back to Spain to live, but I was the only one of our family and group who did. I had a romantic idea about Spain and hoped to go there myself as soon as I finished college, and I thought Agapito felt the same way about Spain. My father and uncles thought that Agapito should ride his luck. He was the only one who knew how to beat the system and he should reinvest his money here and get more of it back, they said. A Spanish house and lands weren't worth the same thing as in America. That was before the Depression but the cigar business had already begun to fall off. Everybody we knew was in trouble and even big *teverianos* like Don Mariano began to complain softly. Only Agapito did well. He did as fabulously as ever, and it seemed more than ironic to my family that he should continue to send his money home instead of trying to get into the "big" money. When the Depression came and the big money blew up into nothing, Agapito's house and lands were still worth very much the same, and his money—which had been kept at home in Spain in the old style—wasn't in a bank that closed.

There was too much fear and bitterness all around for me to feel good about being right, and I couldn't even feel that "I told you so," but the true security of Spain seemed even stronger to me then. I knew I wouldn't be able to go, now—I doubted if I'd even be able to go to college—but I resented the fact that I'd been hearing so much talk about Spain all my life and that only Agapito of the talkers had meant it.

Agapito was a Spaniard and he lived in Spain. America was the place he worked in; being a *teveriano* was just a job that he did well. He had no illusions about America, and so he hadn't been disappointed or fooled as we all had. (The fact that there was a worse depression in Spain didn't occur to me, because I never thought of Spain as a "capitalist" country subject to the same economic laws as our own. Spain was a timeless medieval place of old stone buildings, bullfights and dark-eyed women.)

I felt bitter at not being able to go away to a famous college and I did envy Agapito's good fortune, but it was hard for me to feel bitter against Agapito personally as many Spaniards did. I could see how generous he was—to Grandmother and to many other members of the Spanish colony. Besides, this was the time when I learned that Agapito's famous expression, "If it should ever come to pass that you need . . ." truly meant what it said. This was the way he had closed most of his long stories to me. No matter what the subject, at the end he would say, "Of course, if it should ever come to pass that you need any help in these matters, just come to me. I still have many friends in . . ."

Toward the end of my first year at City College, it did come to pass that I needed his help. This was in a matter that we had never talked about, but I thought of Agapito's constant reminder and at the end, in sheer desperation, I took a chance and went to him.

My best friend had gotten a girl pregnant and neither he nor the girl could see any way out of the mess. He had no money for an abortion, and he didn't want to get married. He was an English major and very high strung, and I thought he was just being melodramatic when he talked about suicide as the way out. He would not be trapped by marriage and a child, he said. Death was preferable. I let him rave and tried to think of a way to raise some money. I got frightened when I saw that he was hoarding some pills of pure codeine. I called him a blown-up bastard and told him that if he'd only shown before one per cent of the care he was showing now, he wouldn't be in this hole. I took the pills with me and told him I'd have something positive arranged in twenty-four hours. I went to see Agapito the next morning.

From the very beginning of the trouble I had thought of going to Agapito for help. He was the most generous person I knew, but, more importantly, he was the only one who had the means to pay for an abortion. I thought he might also have the knowledge to arrange for one—that was very important to me because, even if I'd had the money, I wouldn't have known the first step to be taken in arranging for the operation. The only other person who could have helped me in that—my friend Luz, who was a nurse —had told me to keep my hands off and not to dare get involved in such a thing.

I had hesitated in going to see Agapito because he might very well feel the same way. He was a very moral man, in spite of all the illegal things he was supposed to have done and the brazen way he went about selling. He might truly believe that an abortion was immoral and unnatural as well as dangerous, and that a man who had been stupid and careless enough to get a girl pregnant should take the consequences and stand by the girl. I had often felt like that myself during these last few days.

There was another reason why I had hesitated—I wondered if Agapito would help me as myself. Before, when I had seen his wonderful generosity at work, Grandfather had always been involved. Agapito had made me feel that we were all three working together, but I knew that it was all for Grandfather and that I was just there as "the boy." Grandfather was dead now, and I wasn't a boy anymore. I was a man going to college—I certainly felt like one—and Agapito might remind me of this. He might tell me that I was a man now, and that I had to work out problems by myself as other men did. When he had said to me that if it should ever come to pass that I needed help I should come to him, he had been speaking to me as a boy he cared for, as the favorite grandson of Grandfather, but that I was a man now and would have to learn to shift for myself.

I was still worried about these reasons when I finally did go to see Agapito that morning, but I knew that Gerry was desperate and I felt that I had to do something. Gerry was a particular friend of mine, a new type of friend. He himself had worked to make the friendship, and this was the first time such a thing had ever happened to me. I was very flattered by his attention.

I felt responsible for Gerry, too. At the time we first met he had been a virgin, and I had played the big man of the world when we talked about sex. He hadn't followed my advice about going after an older woman, but he had actually used one of the tricks I'd told him about in the seduction of his girl. I was so embarrassed when he told me that I couldn't even get angry at him.

I went to see Agapito in his room. I told him the whole story immediately. I had intended to be vague about some details, thinking that he might assume then that it was I who was in trouble and be more impressed, but once I had begun to talk I decided to tell him the truth. I made Gerry's predicament very strong.

When I had finished, Agapito shook his head.

"Poor young one!" he said. "Poor young one! Abortions are very dangerous things, *nené*—very dangerous." He patted my shoulder.

"Very expensive, too," I said. I was so relieved to see that Agapito was sympathetic that I was almost flippant in saying this. "That's the thing."

"There is no worry about that. No, I have the money," Agapito said. "I have that. And you can assure your friend that if I arrange this, it will not be dangerous." He pressed my shoulder as he said this and accented the words "your friend." I didn't know what this meant until much later on. "It will be serious," he said, "yes, but not dangerous. Tell your friend to be assured of that."

"Yes."

He asked me about the girl, and I told him that she was willing to have the abortion. "But on the question of the money, Agapito . . ." I said.

*"Nené!"* he interrupted, making a stern face. "That will come later—if at all. Later."

"We're going to pay you," I said. "I'm making this my responsibility."

"Don't worry yourself," Agapito said. "Please! Here, now." He took a business card out of his pocket and wrote a phone number on the back of it. "Call me at this number this evening," he said. "I'll be there all evening."

"Thank you, Agapito," I said. "You know how much I thank you."

"Please, *nené!*" He put his arms around me in an embrace.

I tried to see Gerry immediately but we didn't meet until after the last class. When I told him the news he seemed relieved, but he wasn't as impressed as I thought he should be. I started to get angry but I held myself in. I remembered there was still a long way to go.

When I called Agapito that night, he told me that he had arranged everything. It was to be on the next afternoon, and we were to meet him at the Seguidilla, a restaurant that both he and I knew well. Gerry was still in that same state—dazed and almost bored—when I talked to him that night, and when he behaved the same way the next morning I decided to take the girl to the restaurant by myself. I told Gerry to stay in his room and rest or go to classes—I would cut my afternoon classes.

I met the girls in front of the restaurant—the girl had her best friend with her, with whom she was going to spend the night and who would also accompany her to the doctor's now. I was suddenly relieved on that point—I had been afraid that I would have to go to the doctor's. When we went into the restaurant, we found that Agapito had taken a quiet corner table, apart from the luncheon crowd, and he was so much his gracious self that the introduction went off very easily. There was still some tension and embarrassment as we ate, but it wasn't anything like what I had feared. Prohibition was still on, but Agapito had managed to get some drinks and these helped a lot.

I left them as Agapito and the girls got into a taxi. I went back to the college to do some studying and then stalled until after dinner. I didn't want to sit waiting in the rooming house with Gerry. I went there after seven, and the girl friend called about eight o'clock. She told Gerry that his girl was resting. She said the girl was feeling a little weak, but that everything seemed okay. Gerry was crying when he came up to tell me. At last he could relax.

The next night we learned that the girl had gone to her afternoon classes. She called Gerry herself from her home while her parents were out. She said she felt fine and was in a relieved, happy mood.

I went to see Agapito the next day to report the good news to him and to thank him again. I promised him that I would see to it that my friend paid him back, in full, but he shook his head and again said No, that I should forget all about it. I or my friend mustn't even think of it as a debt, he said. He really smiled very broadly this time when he said "my friend," and I suddenly realized that he thought all the talk about Gerry was just a story and that I was the man in the case. He had never seen Gerry, I remembered, and using the disguise of a "friend" for oneself in a case like this was an old trick—although I had certainly never intended that here.

I tried to reconvince Agapito, but he smiled very openly now and pressed my shoulders. "Young one!" he said. "It's nothing to be ashamed of. These things happen to every man. Don't be ashamed of it. She's a sweet cute girl," he said. "You have good taste."

"But, Agapito, listen—" I tried to say.

"No, no!" he said. "We won't talk about it anymore—about any of it." He patted my cheek, and smiled—as if he were proud of me. "It's finished, and it's finished well."

I was never able to convince him of the truth, then

or later. He persisted in believing that I was the man. Some weeks later I heard that he had told the story to a few of the men in the colony, very discreetly—as if it were flattering to me. I appreciated that part of his attitude, but I was glad that he never told any of the women so that Grandmother or Mother might hear about it.

Many years later, when I was in the Army, I met the girl again and we had lunch together. When we talked about "the mess," she said, "The last part—the part that I worried about most—turned out to be the easiest. That Mr. Lopez was so reassuring, and so charming! He made me feel so safe." She had told me that she was happily married now and had two nice children but, she said, "If I'd only been a little smarter, then—wiser, I mean. I would have become friendly with Mr. Lopez. He could have been so helpful to me—and without hurting me. Oh, he was such a nice man—*and so charming!*"

I had to smile when the girl said "charming" so seriously, and then I explained to her. It wasn't that I doubted Agapito's ability to charm—no one in the Spanish colony ever did—but the subject of his being charming to outsiders or Americans was always the source of laughter or embarrassment to us. He was either so blatant or so skillful that you blushed or smiled for him, according to the way you felt. I liked him and often laughed, but my father and uncles were nearly always sarcastic.

One of the best examples of this was the time

when license renewals came up. Since the early twenties, *teverianos* had had to take out peddler's licenses, and we were Agapito's chief reference. The police captain who came to our house to check this was always a different one because Agapito moved around so, but the captain was always very courteous and solicitous about him. He wanted to get the application cleared up quickly, he would always explain, because Mr. Lopez was a nice man. A very nice man!

"I bet he gave him some tip," my father would say.

"Yes, and if they only knew what a crook he was," my uncle would answer.

I thought Agapito had given him a tip, too, but I knew that wasn't the whole story. He had charmed the hard-boiled captain—as well as so many others.

The only time that his charm ever backfired on Agapito was the only time he ever got into trouble. This was a situation that was out of his field—he should never have been in it in the first place. Agapito had sold cigars, Panama hats, Spanish shawls and many other things that could easily be misrepresented, but he had never dealt in this particular product. The situation was a strange one for Agapito because he was not an evil man—as the selling of this particular product might imply—but I still remember it more clearly than many of his typical cases. It was the best example we ever had of how far Agapito's charm could carry him and how skillful he was at pulling out of a delicate situation.

It had happened many years before—before the Depression, before Grandfather died—and I remembered it for many reasons. One of these was that it led to my second—and last—selling trip with Agapito. That had come indirectly, though, and had nothing to do with the case.

In the colony it was always known as the big "Singapore Platinum Mine" deal. The title is ironic but it was Agapito who originally named it. We heard of it immediately because Grandmother and my father were character references for Agapito in this investigation. The deal had started on the ship as Agapito was returning from Spain after the birth of his third son. He was traveling second class this time but, as usual, he spent most of his time in the first-class salons. The cut of his good suits was much more natural to him now and he wore them well. He never gambled on ships, but he loved to sip brandy and talk with important-looking people. On this trip he met a Mr. Desmond, an English gentleman born in Gibraltar who spoke Spanish as well as a native.

Mr. Desmond was the European representative of a Cuban cigarette company and, after a few nights of confidential talk with Agapito, in which they both freely discussed some of the more daring tricks of their trade, he said he felt sure that Agapito was a gentleman who thought pretty much along the same lines as he. Mr. Desmond then told him of a little trick he was going to work in the States. An old school chum had some platinum holdings in the Far East and the platinum market being what it was, he often made off-the-record shipments to his customers. Mr. Desmond helped him in this, disguising the rare metal as wrapped cigarettes and fitting them into ordinary cigarette boxes. Then he would deliver them to his friend's customers along his route. This time, the first stop was to be at New York. It wasn't really immoral, he explained, just avoiding taxes and, of course, the money was very good.

He showed Agapito such a box the next night, opened one of the cigarettes and displayed the metal bar. It was so light, Agapito said, so very light, that he could hardly feel it on his hand, but he could not bend it. Mr. Desmond laughed at his efforts and they had another brandy. A box of cigarettes like that, with two rows of five "cigarettes," Mr. Desmond explained, was worth twenty-five hundred dollars. Agapito, of course, was amazed and showed it. He asked Mr. Desmond some questions about his friend in the Far East and Mr. Desmond talked for a long time about Malaya and the British Empire and the international fraternity of "right" Englishmen, who were above petty laws. Agapito didn't understand much about this—he knew nothing about the Far East—but he liked the sound of the word "Singapore" in Spanish and always spoke of the Singapore Platinum Mines in telling the story.

As a gentleman, Agapito felt that he should show only a courteous reserve whenever he met Mr. Desmond on shipboard walks during the day, and this reticence seemed to impress Mr Desmond who continued to seek him out for confidential talks at night. Two nights before they were to dock in New York, Mr. Desmond arranged for them to be drinking brandy in a quiet corner of the first-class salon. Mr. Desmond said he wanted to take Agapito into his complete confidence. Agapito said that he was honored. Well, it happened, Mr. Desmond said, that the last time he'd been in New York the police had heard of his platinum deliveries and had talked to him about it. He'd just had to pay a small fine, of course, but they had warned him that the next time they might be much tougher with him. Agapito would understand all this, of course. He knew how the police were. Anyway, Mr. Desmond hadn't been looking forward to his deliveries in and around New York this time and when he met and came to know Agapito he began to get an idea—an idea that would be profitable to them both. He would ask Agapito to do it for him; he was convinced that Agapito was an honest, trustworthy man, and he would present his case to him frankly. He was sure that Agapito would understand—as he did, of course! Agapito said he would be glad to do it, even though he realized there was some peril—a gentleman's peril.

Of course, Mr. Desmond said. But Agapito seemed so skillful at this sort of "harmless masquerade" that it would be nothing for him. And Mr. Desmond would give him a thousand dollars for delivering five packs of the cigarettes. That was too much, Agapito thought. Oh no, Mr. Desmond insisted; he had decided on that sum. He explained to Agapito that the deliveries were all in the general New York area and that no real traveling would be required. He would give Agapito a list of the names and addresses tonight and Agapito would memorize them and give him back the list the next night. Mr. Desmond didn't want any possible embarrassments for Agapito, just in case he should be questioned by the police. Agapito agreed and took the list.

The next night he showed Mr. Desmond that he

had all the names well memorized, and Mr. Desmond gave him the cigarettes in sealed packages and a thousand dollars American. He told Agapito that he thought they shouldn't be seen together the next day—in case there were any customs spies coming on the boat. He gave Agapito a box number in Havana, but told him not to use it unless it were absolutely urgent. Agapito agreed and they parted very good friends. Mr. Desmond promised Agapito that he would keep in touch with him and was sure that they would be doing business again soon.

Agapito got through the customs very easily, with some of the packs on his person and a couple of them placed haphazardly in his luggage. He began to make his "deliveries" immediately, and he was charmed and pleased to see what gentlemen Mr. Desmond's customers were. The first two had fine, plush offices and there was a courteous exchange, the handing over of the pack of cigarettes, a drink of brandy or bourbon, some small gentlemanly talk, firm handshakes and good-bys. Agapito felt proud to be moving in such a world. His third customer was located in Connecticut, about an hour out of New York, and Agapito was surprised to find that this one was not a gentleman—anything but.

Agapito described this one as a little "foreigner" who spoke English with a marked accent. He would not let Agapito into his house, but went quickly back in to get his coat and then walked with Agapito to a dark corner of the street. "Mr. Desmond go to hell! You tell him," he kept saying. "Mr. Desmond go to hell. No more stuff for me! You tell him."

"Certainly!" Agapito kept saying. It was one of the

few English words he could say coldly and, he thought, haughtily. "Certainly!"

The little foreign man moved further back into the shadow and reached into his coat for an envelope. He pushed it toward Agapito. "Twelve thousand dollar, there," he said. "For Mr. Desmond. And Mr. Desmond go to hell! No more Mr. Desmond! No more stuff. For me, you tell him."

"Certainly!" Agapito said, even more coldly. He was shocked at seeing so much money, but he wouldn't let the frightened little man see it. "Certainly," he said.

"You go, now," the man said. He pushed him away. "You forget me. Forget my name. You be sure for that! And Mr. Desmond go to hell!" He pushed again, but Agapito had already started to walk off.

Agapito put the money in his pocket, and felt his neck tingling as he walked away. He wasn't afraid of the man, he said, but he had caught the man's fear. He didn't feel safe until he was in the station. Then, he began to think. He began to think terrible thoughts. The first two customers had been fine, courteous gentlemen and he'd been pleased to meet them. They were just what he'd thought Mr. Desmond's friends would be, and Agapito had felt free and easy, and glad to be in their world. But this fellow in Connecticut was a different story. He wasn't anything like a gentleman, Agapito said. He couldn't speak English, and he was crude and boorish.

Agapito began to doubt Mr. Desmond. No true gentleman would have any kind of dealings with a person like that customer in Connecticut. He began to think over his complete relationship with Mr. Desmond, and when he was finished he acted quickly. As soon as he got back to his rooms, he opened the two remaining packs of "cigarettes." There was no platinum in the cigarettes. Instead, there was a white powder, sealed in a separate paper container in each of the cigarette bodies. There was tobacco at both ends of the false cigarette tubes. That was very clever, Agapito thought, but he was very much afraid of the white powder. It was too late to do anything that night, but he got up early and was down at the Customs Office before it opened. As soon as he could get to see "a man in an office," Agapito told his complete story—omitting the detail about the thousand-dollar fee Mr. Desmond had given him (he thought he deserved that) and not mentioning the first two customers. "I would have told everything, later, if necessary," Agapito said, "but first I wanted to spare those two gentlemen."

The white powder turned out to be heroin, and Agapito had to retell his story for two higher officials. He gladly gave the name of the "gangster" in Connecticut, and told the names of the two people who were to receive the remaining two packs of cigarettes. He also gave the box number that Mr. Desmond had given him. Agapito had to be investigated, of course, but he expected this. The officials had been so convinced by him that they apologized for this point. They asked him to name his own references, and Agapito was permitted to go home that same afternoon.

"My rooms were searched," he said, "I know. But it was done very neatly and quietly. And I was followed for a few days—I saw that, too, but I was never embarrassed." Agapito told me that he had been very tense during the first hours at the Customs Office, but once, during his talk with the second official, he had had to work to keep from smiling. He was answering questions about Mr. Desmond, and the official said, "I'm sure that isn't his name, of course, but we'll still keep calling him that."

"You see, I hadn't given Mr. Desmond my right name, either," Agapito said to me. "I had gotten so used to giving a false name as a *teveriano* that I did it almost instinctively there. And when the official said that about Mr. Desmond, I wanted to laugh. I couldn't even smile, though, as you can understand, and I couldn't tell the official that I hadn't told Mr. Desmond my right name."

One detail that Agapito never explained—not even to me—was the matter of the "twelve thousand dollar" the "foreigner" had given him. He never said what had happened to it. I didn't much care, myself—I believed that Agapito was glad to get out of the mess, no matter how—but this detail of the money intrigued my family. Aunt Elvira tried to get Grandfather to ask Agapito about it. Grandfather had been named by Agapito as one of his references, but he angrily refused to ask about the money. "That money is the concern of Agapito and the officials," he told his daughter. "It is no concern of yours."

Mother tried to get my father to ask Agapito about it, but Father refused. "Ask him yourself," he said. "It's no business of mine."

"Of course, it's your business," Mother said. "He

named you as a reference, didn't he? I only wish he'd named me."

"What would you do—ask him for half of it?" Father said.

"No! I'd make him give it back. Of course I would!" Mother said, but you could see that she didn't really believe that.

The money was the thing most people remembered about the case. They assumed that Agapito had kept the twelve thousand dollars, especially since the construction of his house in Spain began to move ahead very fast in that period, and he went back to Spain after six months instead of a year. "Looking for another Mr. Desmond," my uncle said. "After all, if there are platinum mines in Singapore there can be diamond mines in Manila—right in the back streets."

"Yes," my Aunt Elvira said. "And it's tough to get them through customs, too."

Others in the Spanish colony said equally mean things. Nobody doubted that Agapito really hated heroin and its peddlers, but they were sure he had kept the money and they felt he should have told the whole story—with a complete list of customers, gentlemen or not. At the time, I wasn't old enough to realize the moral implications of heroin or its peddling and of course I hadn't heard the full story from Agapito himself, but I secretly sympathized with his attitude toward "gentlemen" and I believed that Agapito had truly been thrown off by the fact that the Connecticut customer was not a "gentleman." Agapito and I must think of gentlemen in the same way, I thought—a gentleman was above the ordinary problems and emotions of everyday people—and I applauded Agapito for admiring such powerful characters and wanting to be one himself.

I had begun to like Agapito again, even before this, and I'd almost completely forgotten the terrible disappointment I'd felt in him after my first selling trip with him and Grandfather. I didn't admire him in the same complete way I had as a young boy, but I found that he had a lot of good basic points to his character. One of these was the persistence he showed in helping Grandfather and Grandmother. Grandfather often made it difficult for him, but Agapito always devised some new trick to get the money to him. I went on my second and last selling trip with Agapito because of this perverse attitude of Grandfather's.

All through the Platinum Mines case, Grandfather had curtly but steadfastly defended Agapito to my aunts and uncles—and, I imagine, to the investigators who came to question him—but he had some doubts about Agapito himself. He never told me this, but I knew how honorable Grandfather was and how little of a cynic. He had been accustomed to go out selling with Agapito from time to time—a thing he'd been doing since he'd first met Agapito—but after the Platinum Mines case he made excuses to avoid this and did not go out with him again.

Agapito, on the other hand, felt very grateful to Grandfather for defending him in the case. This was a time when he especially wanted to help him. He knew that Grandfather was short of money, as he usually was, and that there was a rent payment coming due very soon. Agapito could not offer the money directly to my grandfather. He had never done that before because he knew of Grandfather's pride, and he certainly would not dare do it at this time lest Grandfather think it was some kind of thanks or payment for defending him in the case.

Agapito tried some clever ruses, but none worked and he finally came to me. I sympathized with the way he was persevering in his effort to help Grandfather but, more than that, I admired the roundabout, elaborate plan he had conceived in which I would go out selling with him, as a substitute for Grandfather, and thus be in the true position to give the money to Grandfather. It was an elaborate plan but it was essentially so obvious—and so innocent—that I think only Grandfather, Agapito and I could have believed in it. Only Agapito knew it from the beginning, of course, but Grandfather and I accepted the results and felt only admiration for him. We felt gratitude for the money but, more so, admiration for the effort involved.

I was going to high school at the time and Agapito came to the school building to wait for me. When he saw me, he started to wave and smile broadly at me. He told me that this was so I shouldn't think something had happened and that he had come to tell me of some misfortune. I was surprised to see him, but glad. He had brought me some very nice books from Spain and I hadn't had a real chance to thank him. He didn't give me a chance this time either, because he started talking right away and said that he was going to visit some friends on a new French ship that afternoon and he had suddenly remembered how much I loved ships and that I would probably like to go with him. I said I would love to, and he said that I wouldn't have to bother calling home because he had already told my mother that he was coming to meet me. I thought that was fine of him.

On the way down to the ship, we took the subway and I didn't have much of a chance to talk to Agapito, but I did get to thank him for the books. He said that it was nothing, and that he would bring me some more the next time. He was his usual polite self, but he seemed very thoughtful about something. I felt he must still be worried about the Singapore Platinum Mines case, and I decided not to talk too much to him so as not to disturb him.

When we were off the subway and walking down the piers, he said, "Pardon me for being so quiet, but I'm very preoccupied about something."

"That's all right," I said, hoping he wouldn't talk about the case. "It's all right."

"I'm preoccupied about your grandfather, young one," he said. He shook his head sternly. "Your grandfather and your sainted grandmother—mostly about her, of course."

I didn't say anything, but nodded. I watched his face.

"You know how your grandfather and I go out selling together," he said, "from time to time, you know. Sometimes when the rent is due, and he has been unlucky. He is a fine man, your grandfather. A very honorable man, that's why he can't be a lucky salesman. . . . I owe him a good deal from other things, so I go out with him at such times. To use my luck for both of us."

"Yes, I know," I said. I was glad Agapito hadn't mentioned the time we went out together with Grandfather. He seemed to have forgotten about that, and I was glad. "I know," I said, again.

"Now this thing of the case—you know the case I've had, the thing of the Singapores—this has taken up so much of my time that I have not been able to do anything with your grandfather. And he, kind gentleman, does not want me to give him any of my time. I know, because he gives me excuses, and tells me to be very careful these days. Oh, you know, young one, the worries of someone who cares for you!" Agapito looked at me intently as we walked. "You know, you know how your grandfather is."

I knew those weren't the reasons Grandfather wouldn't go out with Agapito, but of course I wouldn't tell him. I nodded and said, "Yes, I know," and tried not to look at Agapito. I wondered why he had started to talk about this—it should be so embarassing to him—and I hoped he would stop. "I know," I said in a much lower voice, trying to keep the anger out of it. "I know."

Agapito sighed very loudly, and when I looked up at him I saw that he was smiling. "Well, that's the thing!" he said, with relief, and spread out his hands. "There it is!" I had the feeling that he had said all those things about Grandfather and himself for some necessary reason, and that now he was glad he had gotten it over with. He certainly acted very glad, and now he was just as he had been when he had come to meet me. He began to tell me about the ship, how he had made a trip to Spain on this ship two years ago and still had some friends among the crew. He said

I probably wouldn't be interested in going to the crew's quarters, but that I could look around the salons and decks and enjoy myself while he went to speak to his friends. I said that would be all right, and he was so pleasant and confident that I didn't feel any suspicion about what he might be planning to do. He did say that he had some cigars for his friends and, when I looked questioning, he pressed his sides to show where they were hidden. "One must always be careful of the customs—and they're only cigars, I assure you!" he said with a sudden laugh.

We had turned the last corner and could see the ship now, sitting at its dock, and I forgot all about anything Agapito might want to do in the sudden thrill of seeing the ship. It was a big one-stacker, and the way the last of the afternoon light touched it made it look like a dream. We lost it for a moment as we went into the pier shed, but then came on it more thrillingly and more closely on the side of the pier. It was a big ship but it had the sleek lines that I'd come to know in French ships, and it looked small and trim and fast, even standing still. We walked down past the big passenger gangplank to a smaller one near the stern. Agapito talked to the guard at this end of the gangplank, and he nodded and let us go up. There were no steps at all on this gangplank and it surprised me when it led right into one of the big salons. All the chairs and tables were stacked in a corner, but the bar was lit and there was a man behind it. Agapito greeted him and bought drinks for us. A whiskey for the bartender and himself and a tall soft drink for me. Then Agapito suggested that I should just walk around and look over the ship as I wished. He was going into the crew's quarters.

I finished my drink as quickly as I could and went out into a small room with a tall stairway and then up that to the deck. There were men working on all parts of the ship, but they didn't pay any attention to me. I knew enough, anyway, from being on ships before to keep out of their way and so none of them paid any attention to me. There was loading going on in the stern hold, but I didn't go near there. Instead I went up on the top promenade deck and stood looking down at the loading. I went as far as the bridge and looked in for a minute, and all the time I was doing these things I was thinking of telling Joe, my older brother, about it. He had been with me the last time we'd been on a ship, but that one had been ready to sail and had been very crowded and we hadn't been able to see much because of all the people milling around.

I must have been looking around for a long time, even though it seemed short, because when I went down to the salon again just to see if Agapito were looking for me, he was standing at the bar and talking to two men in white steward coats. He must have been there for a while, because he sighed deeply when he saw me and he seemed a little drunk. I thought of a lot of things suddenly when I saw that he was carrying a French sailor's suit over his arm and holding the hat with the bright red pompon in one hand. He didn't say anything but patted me on the head, and then said good-by to his friends. I felt even more worried when we started out and down the little gangplank and he still kept the suit with him. He gave the guard some cigars and said something about the suit that I couldn't hear very well. Agapito spoke a sort of French-Spanish to the man and I couldn't understand it clearly, but the guard smiled and shrugged his shoulders.

All during the time we walked through the shed I kept wondering what Agapito wanted with the French sailor suit, but instead of getting worried I began to get angry. He didn't seem to notice, because he kept smiling quietly and nodding at something he liked. When we were out of the shed and had started up the street, I couldn't stand it any more and put my hand on his arm to stop him. "What are you going to do with the suit, Agapito?"

"The suit?" He stopped and faced me and raised his arms. "The suit, *hombre?"* he said. He made the theatrical gesture again.

"Tell me as a friend, Agapito," I said very calmly. I did feel very calm, even though I had started out by being angry. "As a friend."

Agapito laughed—with the same relief as before, after he'd talked about Grandfather. "I will tell you," he said. "As a friend—and a fellow worker! That's what I hope we'll be in this—working together. I intended to tell you it was to be cleaned, this suit, and that I might use it. You know, as a costume for just one selling, or for just a few sellings—but I want to tell you the truth, now. It occurred to me some time ago that I could use such a suit, and I asked my friends here for one. They cost very little in our money. I wanted to use it this afternoon with you. Of course I could never do such a thing with your grandfather."

"To use it legally," I said.

*"Hombre,* of course! As legally as we do such things—to sell cigars and to use the suit as an influence. The cigars are there; the suit will impress. That's all. As I say, I would never think of such a thing with your grandfather, but I thought if we went out together I could do it. There would be no risk to you. I assure you I would fix that."

"I don't care about a risk. I don't care, Agapito." I didn't. I was surprised that I could say that, but I wanted to end all this anger and doubt about Agapito; to know what it really was and, if possible, to let it drop—forever. I would see for myself, I thought. I wanted to see, now. The last time I had been out with Agapito I had been too young to understand. I wanted to understand it, now. And there was another reason. I had begun to read Spanish novels and had been amazed at the things boys my age did in those books. They went right into life and did adult things. I felt like a fool when I read about them because I had been afraid to do sexual things or adult things like that and I had reasoned that they weren't for me yet. Going out with Agapito now—with his wearing a disguise—would be that kind of thing and I decided to do it before I had a chance to worry about it.

"I don't care about the risk or the responsibility," I said to him now. "I just don't want you to get into trouble with anybody."

*"Hombre,* I won't. We won't! I say we because we'll be in this together."

"And I will take what Grandfather needs."

"Half, *niño!"*

"No, just what he needs."

We shook hands and started off again, and Agapito put the suit on one arm and put his arm around my shoulder and we walked up the street like that.

We went to the little cigar store first—it was the same one we had gone to with Grandfather. There was a different man there now, but he had the same old color and the same stoop as the other man. He patted my head as if he knew me, but I didn't remember ever seeing him before.

Agapito bought six boxes of cigars and paid seven-fifty for them. The old man put on the same fancy labels as before. I hoped that this time we would have a chance to let them dry.

We left and took the subway to Agapito's room. I waited while he went to the bathroom to change into the sailor suit. His room was nice, very neat, and I studied it. I didn't want to stop to think. I just wanted to go on with this thing and get it over with. When Agapito came out, it was a surprise. He looked fine. He was a handsome man, and the only thing that was wrong was the mustache.

"I can't do anything about the mustache," he said very quickly, as if he could see what I had been thinking. "I won't sacrifice it."

I laughed at him. "You look very nice," I said. "It's a beautiful suit." I particularly admired the hat with the pompon. "It's a real suit."

"You'll see. It will bring us luck," Agapito said. "Yes!" He was reaching for the cigars and holding out his hand to me when the bell rang. It was the downstairs hall bell, and it rang three times—two long and one short—as if it were a signal. Agapito got very red and muttered something. He held up his hand to me and stood by the door to listen. When we heard footsteps coming up, Agapito opened the door and stood waiting. The man who came in had a French sailor suit on, too, but it was an officer's suit—a jacket, and an ordinary hat without a pompon. Agapito shook hands but still looked very sullen. "I wasn't expecting you," he said in Spanish.

"You should have," the man said. "Yes, you should." He closed the door and looked at me.

"This is my friend," Agapito said very clearly. "The grandson of my best friends. You can speak as you wish before him."

The man stared at me for a moment and then took a paper pad out of his pocket. He turned to Agapito and flapped the pad in front of him. "You forgot this," he said.

"Oh, no!" Agapito made the waving gesture with his hands. "Oh, no, I did not!"

"But you took the suit."

"I took the suit to sell cigars. To sell cigars—only that!" Agapito said. "To give it something new; to make it more interesting for the boy—but to sell cigars, only that, and honestly."

The man stared at him, but still held up the book. He used staring the way most people used gestures. He was very impressive he probably thought, but I could see that he was only a petty officer—his coat and pants were very plain and his hat had no embossments. I wondered if he knew what the word "petty" meant.

"I will do that tomorrow," Agapito said into the staring face. He nodded toward the book. "Yes, tomorrow."

"No. We sail tomorrow night. The material must go out tonight." He shook the book and then held it out to Agapito. "There are only five or six more places."

"Where are they?" Agapito said, taking the book.

"Outside of Brooklyn, just outside. The Fulton Elevated to the last stop. They are all in that same vicinity."

Agapito was leafing through the book. It looked like one of the order books that people in the big department stores use. Then he nodded, without looking up. "Good," he said. "All right. I will do it tonight."

The petty officer nodded at him and stared a moment without saying anything. Then he turned to me, nodded and stared, and went out. I thought of him staring at the front door as he went down the stairs, and then up and down the street as he went out.

When I looked at Agapito, he had put the book in one of the big pockets of the sailor pants and had picked up the cigars again. *"Vámonos!"* he said without looking at me. I got up and stood behind him at the door, but he stopped with his hand on the knob and then turned suddenly and pushed me gently back toward the chair. "No, before we go I must explain," he said. "You deserve this, *niño*. I must explain to you."

"About him?" I said.

"About him, about this book." Agapito moved a

chair over near mine. "I had intended to sell only cigars. I swear this to you on your grandmother's soul. I didn't want to have any interference with our going out together. What I told this one about the sailor suit was true. I had intended to do this other thing tomorrow."

"What is that other thing?" I said. No matter what it was, I still intended to go out with Agapito. "It isn't anything like the case, is it? Like the Singapore case?"

*"Hombre,* no!" He pulled back. "I wouldn't do anything like that with you."

"But not about me. What about you, Agapito? It would be very dangerous for you."

"No, no," he said. "It's just liquor."

"Bootlegging?"

"Oh, no! Not that—selling poison and hurting people. This is good liquor from France. It is illegal, yes. But it is not evil. It is not harmful."

"But you're doing it so soon?" I said. "So soon after the other thing."

"There are obligations I have to go through, but I do not put it in that class, *niño*—believe me! I didn't want to do it this afternoon only because I do not want anything of this kind to touch you or your grandfather. And I assure you, *niño*—" he put his hand on my shoulder—"if there is any danger—the slightest—I will not let it touch you."

"The danger is all right, Agapito. I was only thinking of you."

"Thank you," he said and nodded very seriously. "Many thanks. I assure you, though, that I will sell the cigars this afternoon. That is the important thing." He pressed my shoulder and stood up. "We will go now."

We went out together. Halfway down the stairs he stopped and turned to me again. "Will you say anything to Grandfather about this?" he said.

"*Hombre,* of course not!"

"I think it best," he said. "Grandfather would not understand."

"I know."

We shook hands.

We didn't talk on the street or on the el, but I didn't feel embarrassed about Agapito's suit because it really looked very nice. One time he did look at me very definitely and smiled and patted my cheek. "Remember now," he said. "I don't want you in any of this. You serve by just being there."

"All right," I said. "Good." I was determined to go through with it no matter what it was, and I was even feeling a little proud of myself at this time. I was going to do this dangerous thing without thinking about it—and I hadn't even known about it this morning. The money for Grandfather was important, but I didn't even want to think of that now.

As soon as we were at the last stop and were walking down the long el station stairs, Agapito began to play a part. He had put the hat on at a tricky angle and he began to talk to me in his version of French—pretty loudly, too. I couldn't understand him, and I smiled foolishly at him. I didn't see why he was doing this right now, because there was nobody around. It seemed a very lonely place. When we reached the foot of the stairs and came to the street, I could see that there were some stores on the corners, but the streets at the side were all unpaved. There were one-family houses along these streets. The stores on the corners seemed to be all bars, and we went right into the nearest one. These were bars in the period of Prohibition, and you could tell they were bars by the heavy curtains strung along the windows and the glass of the doors. They had no writing anywhere on the windows. Inside they were the same as the old bars except that they had no sawdust on the floors and no whiskey bottles showing by the mirror behind the bar. Everything else was the same except that the smell wasn't so strong.

This one that we went into now, with Agapito pulling me by the hand and closing the door quickly behind us, was big but there weren't many men there. Agapito was smiling and acting, and saying something that sounded like *"alonze"* to me in too loud a voice. I didn't like it, but I didn't get embarrassed, even when he still held on to my hand as we went up to the bar. There were only three men standing at the bar, with another man behind the bar who didn't have an apron on and was dressed in an ordinary suit. They all looked at me.

"My son, my boy," Agapito was saying as we stepped up. "I could not leave him. At the ship, you see."

The man behind the bar nodded. "We have only soft drinks," he said in a very cold voice. It was true because there were ginger ale bottles lined along the mirror of the bar where whiskey bottles used to be.

"Of course!" said Agapito. "Yes. Ginger ale. Ginger ale for two!" The man stood watching us for a moment, then bent down under the bar and brought up two tall glasses. He put some ice in them, and then took one of the bottles of ginger ale from behind him and poured it into the glasses. Agapito handed mine over to me even though I could have reached it easily myself. He smiled at me in that broad way and I nodded to him.

I had forgotten how strange Agapito's costume was, but I began to look at it now because two of the men at the other end of the bar had been staring at him and were smiling. Agapito didn't see them, because he was bending down to reach for the cigar boxes and put them up on the bar. He would not have minded anyway, I think, because he was playing up his part now as he looked at the man behind the bar and patted the cigars. "Good cigars. No customs," he said. He smiled very broadly at the man. "Cheap. Very cheap."

When the man didn't say anything, Agapito said, "You smoke?" and reached to pull out one of the boxes, but the man reached out quickly and put his hand on the box. He shook his head. "No," he said. "I don't smoke, and I don't want to buy any."

One of the men at the other end of the bar laughed, and the man behind the bar smiled. I began to feel angry at them, and a little embarrassed for Agapito, but I tried to hold this last feeling down. Agapito did seem to be stopped for a moment, but then he just shrugged his shoulders, smiled and pushed the box into the pile.

We both took a long sip of the ginger ale—it was flat—and then Agapito put his glass on the counter and reached the cigar boxes down to me. "Go over to the door," he said, in Spanish.

"Wait a minute," the man said to Agapito in a more pleasant voice. "Don't you have anything else to sell?"

"Oh, yes," Agapito said, turning calmly to him. He waited until I'd started for the door, and then he took the order book out of his pocket. He passed it over the counter to the man. His face was very stern. "Oh, yes," he said.

The man took the book and quickly flipped through the pages. He stopped at one and marked it carefully, and then tore out the sheet and handed the book back to Agapito. I knew there was a carbon copy left in that kind of book. Agapito nodded to him, without saying anything. He put the book back in his pocket and came to the door. He did not turn to look back as we went out.

We went into two other bars—the same kind as the first, with curtains on the windows—but almost exactly the same thing happened in these.

Agapito just couldn't get started on the cigars. I knew that he wasn't holding back—he kept putting on a heavier accent at each new place, opened his eyes wider and made even more florid gestures—and instead of feeling embarrassment, I began to feel admiration for Agapito. He really worked hard, and he just wouldn't be discouraged—or insulted.

There was a terrible thing about it, too. The harder he worked on the cigars, the easier it was to sell the liquor. The man at the third bar didn't even let him finish talking about the cigars. "Come on, sailor, don't waste my time," he said. "Let me see the book." Agapito handed him the book without a word, but he looked over at me sadly as the man was writing in it.

I knew how embarrassed Agapito was by this terrible thing. He had to sell the cigars to give Grandfather some money—he wouldn't dare give Grandfather any of the illegal money—and the cigars seemed to have bad luck because of the liquor. Even when we went into a fourth bar—where there was no question of the book because the liquor had been taken care of immediately—Agapito still couldn't sell even one box of the cigars.

He was flushed from acting so hard and blushing, and stopped to adjust his cap to the more rakish angle after we'd come out of the last bar.

"Agapito——" I said.

He raised his finger and then shook it. "No discouragement!" he said. "No discouragement."

I watched him for a moment, and nodded.

Agapito was staring down the avenue where the el ran. There was another store in the middle of the block that had a big sign saying CANDIES AND STATIONERY. Agapito had stared at it for only a moment when he nodded, fixed his cap again and picked up the boxes. *"Allonze!"* he said and held out his hand.

As soon as we got close to it I could see that it was a candy store like the ones in our neighborhood that sold candies and sodas, cigarettes and cigars and papers, and that were run by old people with sad, angry faces. This store was just like them except that the owner wasn't very old, but he was big and heavy and bald and had a very angry face. As we came in, he stood in front of the counter and stared coldly at us even when Agapito had smiled very broadly and bowed. He looked Agapito up and down very carefully and didn't even look at me. "Yes?" he said.

"Cigars?" Agapito said in his Spanish accent. "I buy two cigars." He pointed to the counter at his side.

"You've got a whole bunch of them there," the man said. He pointed at the boxes with his foot. "What d'you want to buy cigars for?"

"Oh, too expensive these," Agapito said, patting the boxes. "Too expensive for me! These to sell." He bent over to look at the cigars in the counter. "I buy others for me. Cheaper." He was looking at the cigars in the counter very seriously as if he were truly interested in buying cigars. "Yes, too expensive for me."

The man watched him for a moment, then sneered loudly. "What d'you mean, too expensive?" he said, and when Agapito didn't turn to look at him he reached out his hand and pulled him around by the arm. "Did you steal 'em?"

"Oh, no!" Agapito said. He stood up very straight. "I buy them in Havana, when the ship stop there. Havanas! Havana cigars!" he said, pointing down to them. He was looking very stern. "I get them through customs—without pay. That's all."

The man stared again. I didn't like him. "How expensive? How much?" he said.

"These, Havanas," Agapito said.

"I know, I know. You told me." The man bent down suddenly and pulled one of the boxes out. He opened it with the nail of his thumb quickly. He was a very big, strong man and he was a bad word, I thought. He took a cigar out and closed the box.

Agapito was watching him with that made-up stern face as he bit the end off the cigar and pulled out a match to light it. Agapito quietly reached the box out from under the big man's arm as he lit the cigar. He took a few quick puffs that made a lot of smoke and then looked at the cigar. "How much?" he said. "They're lousy, you know."

"Havanas," Agapito said. "From Havana."

"They're lousy enough to be Havanas. How much?"

Agapito bent down to the pile and seemed to be counting the boxes. Then he stood up and squinted his eyes. I remembered how he had done the exact same thing the last time I had been out with him many years ago, but this time I wasn't embarrassed for us and I hoped he would make it a big, stiff price. I thought of all the times Agapito must have had to suffer abuse like this, and I hoped he had gotten a lot of money for it. I hoped he was going to get it now.

Agapito opened his eyes wide and looked at the man seriously. "Seventy-two dollars," he said.

Good! I thought. Good!

The man made a face and held the cigar as if he were going to throw it down. "Seventy-two dollars? For six boxes?"

"Twelve dollars each box," Agapito said very evenly. "Twelve dollars each box."

The man stared at him with the cigar held like that. He was trying to frighten Agapito, I thought. "I'll give you fifty dollars," he said. "Fifty dollars for the six boxes."

Agapito reacted just the way I'd hope he would.

He smiled at the man in a superior way and shook his head slowly. "Oh, no," he said. "No."

"Fifty dollars!" the man said.

Agapito shook his head again and bent down to fix the box in the pile. The man walked between us to the glass door and stood there. "Come here, you," he said to Agapito in a gruff voice, and when Agapito stayed bent over the bundle he reached out and pulled him to the door by the arm. He grabbed at his shirt front and pressed him to the door. "See that building over there?" he said, pointing across the street with one of his big hands.

Agapito turned his head slowly to look.

"That's a police station," the man said. "A police station—you get that? Don't sell me the cigars for fifty dollars and I'll take you and the cigars over there. Then, we'll see about customs and who owns the cigars. Then, we'll see. . . ."

He said some more but I couldn't hear it, because as soon as he had grabbed Agapito like that and started to threaten him I picked up the iron bar from the paper stand behind me and ran over to the candy counter. I held the bar over it and yelled at him to get his attention. I was tired of seeing Agapito insulted. I was tired of seeing a Spaniard take it from everybody. Agapito might be a swindler but he was a gentleman, and he had never hurt or insulted anyone. I saw all the insults Grandfather must have taken—and Don Mariano and people like that—and I was tired of them. "Hey, you!" I yelled. "Hey, you bastard—look at this—you let him go or I'll break it. I'll break it—and I'll tell the cops you were trying to hit me. Let him go," I said. "Let him go."

When he turned he was frowning. He crinkled his face and bent down as if he were getting set to spring at me. He was still gripping Agapito's shirt though, and I bit my tongue and held the bar really tight. I lifted it just a little more.

Agapito was holding his hand up at me. "Hold," I heard him say in Spanish. He was speaking very sternly. "Hold, *niño!* Nothing of that." He pulled his shirt out of the big man's hand as he stood up straight. I saw that his face was very stern. "Nothing of that, *niño,*" he said again. "You're out of this."

He brushed off his shirt where the big man had held it and looked up at him sternly. "For fifty dollars," he said, in the same stern voice. "You can have them—the six boxes."

"Fifty dollars," the big man said. He was still frowning, but he wasn't so tense now. "Fifty dollars, okay."

They both looked at me at the same time. I had let my arm down, but I still held the iron tightly. Agapito made a sign with his hand toward the paper stand and nodded. I walked over there and put the iron down, but kept my hand near it. The big man had been watching me and as soon as I put the bar down he made a sneering, laughing sound and picked up the tied boxes of cigars.

He took them in back of the counter, undid the cord and began to open and examine each one. He brought each box to the counter top, opened it and looked through the cigars to make sure that all rows were complete. He kept looking at Agapito and me as he did this. After he had finished he nodded and came around to the front of the counter. He reached under the white apron he was wearing and took a big roll of bills out of his side pants pocket. He counted five tens off the top—they all seemed to be tens—and gave them to Agapito. "I'll sell them for twice that!" he said as he put the bills back in his pocket. "You wait."

Agapito nodded. "You'll sell them well, I know," he said quietly. He folded the money carefully and put it into his pocket, and then reached out his hand to me. Agapito said, "Good afternoon," and nodded to the big man, and we went out into the street. The big man nodded, and then laughed a little.

We didn't say anything as we walked slowly down the street. Agapito put his arm around me and pressed my shoulder. "You were very brave," he said, "but you must not get into trouble for me. No, I could not permit that. Let him have the cigars—and good luck to him! Yes," he said, as if to himself, and nodded.

I was staring at him in such surprise that he looked shocked for a moment and then started to laugh. He laughed very heartily, and kept pressing my shoulder. "You know me," he said, after a moment. "Yes, *niño,* you know me. I was still acting, then. It was a good profit anyway."

"Of course," I said. "That's what I thought."

"But it's the justice of it!" Agapito said. "After I'd thought so hard and planned the story, I deserved what I asked."

"I wanted you to get it," I said. "I truly did."

"I know," he said.

"It's good it ended this way, anyway."

Agapito nodded. We didn't say anything until we reached the foot of the el station. Then he stopped me and took the fifty dollars out of his pocket. Before

I could say anything to protest, he put the money into my shirt pocket and buttoned it.

"But, Agapito——"

"Nothing!" he patted my cheek. "I want you to take it all. I could not touch your grandfather with the money from the other thing—and you have earned this."

"But what about you?"

"I'll have the other soon. I don't need any money for now."

"Are you sure?" I said.

"Yes, *niño*. Yes." He put his arm around my shoulder again and we went up the stairs.

We did not talk on the train because Agapito seemed to be thinking, and I felt very quiet and content. There was one time when he caught me looking at him. "You are not a *teveriano,*" he said, smiling. "No."

"No, and I don't want to be one. I don't like it."

Agapito smiled sadly, and shook his head. "There are some things about it—thrilling things. Yes," he said, sitting up straight suddenly and rubbing his hands. "I must go back to it—entirely back. I want to give up this thing—" he pulled at the sailor shirt—"I don't like this thing. I want to do *teveriano* selling—nothing more." He took off the sailor hat and crushed it in his hand.

"Don't!" I said, before I could stop myself. "Agapito—that hat! It's——"

He stopped and laughed, and smoothed out the hat. "I knew you like it," he said. "Here, take it." He pressed it into my hands. "Take it, *niño*. If I ever use the suit again I can buy another."

# *Chapter Four*

I STILL HAVE THAT HAT, but I never went out with a *teveriano* again and never wanted to. Fortunately I never had to think of it much because Grandfather retired soon after that afternoon without ever going out again. His son, my uncle Joe, had a good job by that time and could help support Grandfather and Grandmother. I did share something wonderful with Grandfather when he came out of retirement to become the Chairman of the Entertainment Committee of La España, but it had nothing to do with *teverianos*.

Agapito was the only *teveriano* of those I knew who continued to work successfully. That was only natural, of course, because he was the best. He stopped selling liquor after the end of Prohibition and then, when the big mass production of cigars seemed to make Havanas a pure luxury, Agapito was still able to find people who could afford them. At other times he sold Spanish shawls that had never been in Spain, Panama hats and mantillas. As with the Havanas, these were all good things, but he sold them at exorbitant prices.

Agapito never had a bad time with money, but other things began to go wrong. When the Spanish

Civil War started he brought his family over here immediately. On the trip his youngest son, the pride of the family, had an attack of appendicitis and had to be taken off the ship at Nova Scotia. Still, the operation was too late and the boy died.

The second youngest son, who was then fourteen, took to American ways immediately. He loved high school—especially track events which he had never seen in Spain—and he became a fanatical athlete with six-o'clock-in-the-morning runs around the nearby park. He caught cold one day, but wouldn't quit on his routine—he had the recent convert's terrible zeal. When it developed into pneumonia, he was taken to the best hospital in New York and was given the new sulfa drugs immediately. It was either too late or they wouldn't take, and the boy died on the fourth day. The illness cost Agapito more than two thousand dollars.

Older people in the Spanish colony began to nod their heads and repeat the old thought that Agapito's money was cursed. It had taken a long time, but more people began to believe it now. I even thought at the time that Agapito himself began to believe it. We had been on opposite sides of the Spanish Civil War, but I had gone to visit the boy in the hospital and then to visit Agapito after the death. "Who knows," he said to me. "It may be true what they say. To lose two sons is certainly to be cursed."

I tried to point out the circumstances of luck to him, and that the money enabled him to help his sons and give them the best care when they did get sick. "Luck," he said. "Yes, maybe that's what I've lost—my luck."

"No, you haven't," I said. "Wait until you go out again."

He was not "going out" at this time because his wife was grief-stricken and he had to be near her. I went to visit him often—I was waiting to be drafted and had quit my job. I felt at that time that I really cared for Agapito and I hoped that his luck as a *teveriano* would hold up. It was more than a question of money to him; it seemed to give him the satisfaction that an artist gets.

Agapito had always seemed so full of life to me that I hated to see how much death was touching him in these last years, but there was still a warm, typically Spanish feeling about all this: the funeral of his second son was the last Spanish funeral I ever attended. The war was coming and I knew that I would be in it. More importantly, the war would put an end to my conception of the Spanish colony, and wakes and funerals had been a very important part of that. I felt sadness for Agapito but more regret at the passing of this period of my life.

Death had always been an important part of life in the Spanish colony. I had felt it as a child, without knowing why. When I began to study Spain and read Spanish authors, I saw that death had always been an obsession with the Spanish people. To the Spaniard, "death, too, is a fiesta," says V. S. Pritchett, and the important thing here is the special meaning that the word "fiesta" has for the Spaniard, and for Pritchett. A "fiesta" is any gathering held for a special purpose, but most of us forget that the purpose may often be a tragic one; so many Spanish fiestas feature black-hooded figures and the bitter memory of death.

At all the wakes and funerals as I remember them, though, there was no bitterness but a coziness and warmth only equaled at big dances and the Sunday night gatherings at Grandmother's. At the wakes, people who hadn't seen each other for years met and embraced and wept, promising each other that they would never let the years pass again without visiting; but I thought that they would not meet again until the next wake, and I believed they thought this, too. Brandy and coffee were always served, but I never saw any drunkenness. (I have seen only one drunken Spaniard in my life and that was in Spain many years later.)

There were two main groups at these wakes: the people in the front room who sat with the family of the dead around the coffin, and the group in the back rooms that could talk more freely. It was understood that everyone should spend some time with both groups but, toward the late hours of the night, the men usually drifted to the back room and the grieving women stayed in the front. I used to like to sit in the back room because you heard more stories there, about *teverianos* and about Spain.

Every wake I remember was crowded, but no Spaniard at any time thought of having the dead placed in an undertaking parlor. Furniture had to be moved to accommodate the people and there was some work arranging for the coffee and sandwiches, but there were always willing friends to take over these chores. Indeed, it seemed to me that the same people used to do these things at all the wakes. That was the only time in their lives when they seemed to have some importance.

I was always terribly afraid of death—as a child, I used to think it could come any night—but still I always enjoyed the Spanish wakes and always wanted to go to them. I think it was because the dead played so living a part in the wake. To be dead didn't seem so terrible to me then. I never heard a Spaniard speak of the dead person as "being with God" or "being in heaven." They were always spoken of in the usual familiar tones as if they were still there. The Spaniard didn't think of the dead person as "asleep"; the dead were dead, but they were still physically here with us. They were still a part of this group of people who loved one another, and they would continue to be so.

And for that reason the funeral was always a definite break, a wrenching. The city outside seemed the starkly alien place that it had always seemed to us, as Spaniards; the Church was embarrassing to the men who went there so rarely, and the dead had finally to be left outside at the cemetery in this separate, alien place. I have heard the most practical Spaniards speak of wanting to be buried in Spain and, at Spanish funerals, I could understand their reasons for this. It had never happened to anyone, of course, but if we ever had a wake here for someone whose body was to be sent to Spain, I thought that the wake would be more like a farewell party or a leave-taking.

At Agapito's son's wake there wasn't a big crowd, because the Spanish colony was really growing smaller and the younger generation didn't pay as much attention to such things, but the brandy was the best and there was more than enough of coffee, cigars and sandwiches. I was sitting in the back room during the late hours of the evening and got into a long and interesting conversation with my neighbor. He was an elderly man and I did not know him but thought that it wasn't strange because I had been away from the colony for a while. After the man left, Agapito's oldest son came over to me and asked me if I knew the man. I said no; I had assumed that he was a friend of the family. "He isn't," the son said, "and I'm glad he left or else I would have had to chase him out."

"*Hombre,* why?"

"He was just a gate-crasher," he said. He was getting very American. "They come for the drinks, and to look around."

"Are you sure?"

"Oh, yes. He was probably some Puerto Rican. You have to be very careful."

Oh, well, I said, I didn't know. But I did know and thought it would be difficult to explain to this "American" boy. The man might have been a Puerto Rican, but he knew what a Spanish wake was and he had come only for the warmth and the company. The best brandy in the world wouldn't be worth the embarrassment, and anyway brandy gives only a physical warmth.

Agapito's luck as a *teveriano* did hold up—I heard some stories about it while I was in the Army—but other things kept going wrong. The house in Spain was just about finished, and his wife was anxious to go there to live. She hated this place where she had lost two sons so quickly, but her two oldest sons had adapted themselves very quickly and wanted to stay. Agapito joined his sons in convincing their mother that it would be better to stay together in America. The big war came and the sons were drafted, but they had been married before that and were happy here.

I saw Agapito only once more. That was when I was on furlough in New York and went to visit my father. Agapito was there and, returning to the city, he insisted on taking me to the door of my apartment in a taxi. I wanted to talk about him and his life, but Agapito insisted on hearing about my Army career. I was only a Pfc., but told him that I preferred that and hoped to avoid any big responsibility. Agapito insisted, however, that if it ever came to pass that I should decide to go to officers' school, I had only to tell him. He would fix it for me; he had good friends in the Army. He probably had, I thought, as I tried to keep from smiling, and I knew that was one thing that hadn't changed in Agapito because he made the offer as sincerely as he had made the first one to me so many years before.

Agapito died just before V-J day. I heard later that he had died quietly at home after a short illness, with the sounds of his grandchildren's voices in the next room. The oldest grandson, of course, was named Agapito. Agapito's wife had died a year before, and he was buried with her and his two sons in their family plot in a new cemetery in Queens. He had never gotten back to Spain to live.

His dream house, in fact, had been given away. Just before she died his wife had made Agapito promise that he would turn over the house to an order of nuns in the nearby city. It was too late for Agapito and her to enjoy it, the wife said, and the children didn't want it. And Agapito could afford it, anyway.

Agapito complied with her wish. He paid for the final furnishings and turned the house over to the nuns. It became a home for wayward girls who had become pregnant, and this was a fact that afforded one of his false friends a final chance for making a nasty joke about Agapito. It was most appropriate for the house to become such a thing, the man said, because Agapito's contributions alone might have filled it. This was a canard, but I'm sure Agapito must have smiled his wise, knowing smile when he heard it.

I thought it was singularly appropriate, too, but for other reasons. I had a much more realistic attitude toward Spain now and I knew the gloomy fate that faced most unmarried pregnant girls—especially those in the populous servant class. Even one small contribution of help, I thought, was a big one.

There was a more personal reason for my approval, too: I remembered the time of Gerry's trouble with his girl—how desperate I felt, how completely Agapito had come to our aid! I remembered the confident, secure feeling he had given Gerry's girl, and I knew there would be many girls now who would get some of that same safe feeling in the home that had been made out of Agapito's dream house. He had built himself a monument, without intending to, because the home would dispense that best quality of his, long after his death. It would reach out that quick and assuring generosity that Agapito himself had shown us so often.

Recalling him now, I remember that quality well. His generosity is still alive—while the many embarrassments he caused me are dead, boring things—and the childish fantasy that I often use to evoke Agapito's memory has to do with his kindness. It is ridiculous, as most fantasies are, but unlike so many of them it has a basis in fact.

I think of a little Spanish servant girl in Galicia, sitting alone in her bare four-by-five room, cold with fear and the dread of her certain pregnancy, unmarried and abandoned and alone as such a girl can be alone only in Spain and in Dickens. There is a knock on her door and the startled girl whispers, "Who?" Then, "Come in."

When she sees the handsome stranger—flagrantly over-dressed in a light-colored suit with shirt and tie to match, and carrying a Panama hat and a cane—the girl has the sudden hysterical thought that she has already been made a prostitute and that this tourist is an admitted customer to her "rooming house." She starts to moan until Agapito quickly reassures her. He is a friend who seeks nothing, he tells her. He sits on the bed beside her and takes her hand. She has nothing to worry about, he explains—she and the baby will be taken care of. Yes, it will be arranged very simply. She need only call the telephone number that he will give her and she will be immediately admitted to the Santa Teresa Retreat for Girls, which is a nice, clean, modern building on a high hill in the western part of this same province. There she will get care, sunshine, good food and good advice.

As soon as Agapito has calmed the girl, he writes down the telephone number for her, gives her whatever money she will need for carfare, meals and "perhaps a new dress," and then prepares to leave. In a moment of sudden inspiration, he reaches into his coat pocket and brings out a bracelet of hammered Mexican silver which he presents to the girl with a gracious bow. She is to wear this with her new dress. This is a holiday trip she is taking—not a sad and dreary one.

As the girl smiles for the first time, Agapito is pleased and smiles back. He is glad he remembered the bracelet, and he will not miss it. The piece is a spare from the four lots of imitation hammered Mexican silver that he has purchased wholesale from a distributor on Fourth Avenue in New York, and which he is presently selling—at his usual exorbitant prices—to the wives of many *nouveau riche* industrialists of northern Spain as genuine examples of native Mexican jewelry.

He pats the smiling girl on the cheek, and takes up his hat and cane to leave. Just one thing more, he says. He hopes that the girl will listen to the good advice they give her at the home, and that she will be more careful in the future. But even so, and no matter what, she must never worry—for if it should ever come to pass again. . . .

# PART TWO

# The Good Pair

# *Chapter Five*

THERE WAS A TIME when I thought Grandfather and I would never be together again. He would never need me again, I thought. He had stopped selling cigars a long time ago and so he did not need a guide or translator, but we never even went out for walks together now. Grandfather stayed mostly at home, and I saw him only when I went to visit. That wasn't often, because I was in third year of high school at the time, with a difficult program, and had to study very hard. I began to think of myself as grown up and as an American, and to feel that Grandfather was old and definitely retired, when suddenly he became the chairman of the Entertainment Committee of La España, the Spanish benevolent society in Brooklyn. Every Spaniard we knew belonged to La España, and the chairman of the Entertainment Committee was the most important man in the society.

Grandfather had been associate chairman for over twenty years—he was elected automatically with Mariano Benitez as chairman—but since Grandfather was a meek and retiring man he never took part in the real and the interesting work of the committee. Grandfather would arrange for the printing of the tickets and the programs and the decorations in the hall, but the big things like the hiring of the orchestra and the entertainers and the escorting of the entertainers while they were in the city were always done by Don Mariano.

Don Mariano was almost as old as Grandfather, but he was a bright, cheery man and a wise man, and he was one of the most successful *teverianos* in the history of the colony. He was a very flashy dresser, and I know that the women in the colony thought he took too intimate an interest in the female entertainers he escorted around the city. Nobody said anything about this to his wife, Doña Emilia, who was a sad, quiet woman, and of course the men in the colony never paid any attention to it. I think they understood it.

When Don Mariano had had a heart attack a few years before, he had delegated Agapito to take over the important work of the Entertainment Committee. Agapito, who was very much like Don Mariano and was a pet of his, did a fine job, and so when Don Mariano died suddenly in Chicago that summer everybody thought that Grandfather would automatically assign Agapito to do the important work—the entertainment was not even arranged for. Instead, Grandfather assumed the chairmanship himself and said that he would take over the "executive" work.

"You, an executive?" Grandmother said scornfully.

"Papa, you're just being stubborn," my mother said. "You can't do it. You're no good at these things."

"I can do it," Grandfather said. "I can do it—in some way." Later, he said to Grandmother, "Now that I'm sure I will never go back to my own country, I want to do something in this one. Something worthy of me."

I had come over with Mother and I was still there when Grandfather said that. "I'll help you," I said. I felt a sudden rush of the old feeling I'd had for Grandfather when I saw how alone and brave he seemed. "I'll help you in this thing if you want me to."

"Much thanks!" he said. "I do want you to. Yes, I will need your help."

Grandmother looked at him and then stared at me. "Well, you two are together again," she said in her cold voice. She looked very tall and dignified.

"Yes, and we're a good pair," Grandfather said. He seemed to shrink physically before Grandmother's coldness, but he said this very surely and strongly. "A good pair. Yes!"

"Like the last time, José?" Grandmother asked coldly. "The last time you two were a good pair? Do you recall that?"

"Yes, I do. I do recall that," Grandfather said sternly. "I do recall that, but I don't want to speak of it now. We should not."

Grandmother stared at him. Then she shrugged her shoulders and went out, without looking at me. Grandfather came over and smiled and patted my shoulder. "Tomorrow then, young one?" he said. "I will come to see you."

"Any time you wish, Grandfather," I said.

He pressed my shoulder as I stood up. I hated to

leave now, but I could see that Grandfather was very definite. He walked to the door with me and I didn't even go into the kitchen to say goodnight to Grandmother. I hated to leave because I knew that as soon as I was out Grandfather would have a very unpleasant argument with Grandmother about the "last time" he and I had been called a "good pair."

That was a little over a year before, when Grandfather had been my only defender in what Grandmother always referred to as "that horrible matter."

I had been going to high school for two years then, and had begun to think of myself as a man—especially since the day my grade adviser had discussed college requirements with me. The thought of college alone had filled me with hope and a new importance and, though I knew that the coming third year was going to be a tough one, the free summer was here now and I had lots of spare time to be happy in. I used to go for many walks with Grandfather in the park. On our way back, we would often stop at the house of the widow Martinez who lived near the park. She was very nice, and served us hot chocolate and crackers. Though it was summer, it was very cool and comfortable in her rooms, and the hot chocolate tasted good. Grandfather enjoyed these visits very much—and I did, too.

Before, I had always thought of the widow Martinez as being old, like Grandfather and Grandmother. But when I looked at her closely, I saw that she wasn't that old and that she had beautiful eyes and a lovely, smooth skin. She had always seemed like a fat lady to me, but now that I saw her in the thin summer dresses that she wore, I thought that she had a wonderful figure. She looked like one of those Lachaise statues I had seen in my Art Appreciation textbook, if the statue had had on a long black summer dress, tied tightly at the waist. She still seemed big, but the bigness was exciting now. She was a very quiet woman, and she looked quickly down every time I stared at her.

After the second visit, I had begun to think of her all the time, especially at night. I wanted to see her alone, but didn't know how to arrange it. Once when Grandfather had forgotten a package, I ran back to her rooms to get it and, as I was leaving, I leaned over suddenly and kissed her on the cheek. She smiled and patted my face. I wanted to reach my arms around her, but I had the package in one hand and the knob of the door in the other.

The Monday after that, Mother went to the beach with my younger brothers and sisters, and I knew that Grandfather wasn't expecting me. As soon as I could get away, I went over to the widow Martinez's. I was afraid that she would be very surprised or even offended to see me alone like this, but she was only a little embarrassed and made me sit down right away. She seemed embarrassed about the fact that she didn't have a black dress on and that she had a cap over her hair. I told her she looked very beautiful before I could stop myself. She had on a light house dress and it made her look very exciting. I knew that widows were always supposed to wear black, but I hoped that she wouldn't go and change.

"You're very beautiful," I said. "You're not an *old* widow."

"I am. Yes, I am," she said. "But, all right, if you

won't say that you saw me in this dress, I won't worry myself about it."

"No, I won't say anything. I won't say anything about the dress or about being here."

"Oh," she said. "That, too?" She patted my cheek. I wondered why she didn't smile, and why she looked so serious.

When she came back with the hot chocolate, she had her hair combed up, but she had not changed her dress. When she sat down beside me on the big couch and bent over to pull the little table with the tray closer, I caught a sudden deep scent of her perfume. It was a light, incenselike perfume, but I felt it go right through me and make my heart beat even faster. I had suddenly felt warm and my heart had begun to beat hard the moment she came and sat down beside me, and now it was beating harder than ever. My hand reached out to her shoulder before I could stop it. She turned slowly to stare at me, with her hands still on the table, and then smiled and came back slowly with my arm still around her. I leaned over quickly and kissed her on the lips, without stopping to think that this was wrong and a sin maybe, and I felt her breasts with a sudden burning against my chest before I touched her lips that were surprisingly soft, but seemed to be moving. I pressed my mouth hard on them and reached my hand down to her hips, and almost pulled it away in sudden fright because there she was! Where I had expected to find a corset or some kind of heavy girdle, my hand felt the full roundness of her hip through the thin material of the dress. The touch of the skin was there and real, and my hand clenched into her. I clutched more tightly when she brought her hand down on mine and tried to pull it away. I could only think of one thing—how big and wonderful she was there—and my hand began to tingle as I jerked it quickly away from hers and moved it, clutching at her behind and trying to press her close to me as I leaned over on to her, but her hand went up to my shoulder suddenly and pushed me away as she pulled her head back and stopped the kiss.

*"Nené!"* she said very sternly. I could see that she was only fooling. *"Nené!"* I tried to look serious too, but I had to smile suddenly, I felt so good. She gave me a quick peck of a kiss, and sat up very straight and started to fix the back of her hair.

I can do it, I was thinking. I can do it! I can! I can! All the thoughts about sin and immoral actions and how I shouldn't do anything like this until I was married were pushed far away. I felt so good, I felt I was stepping on them. I can do it, I thought. I'm in that world.

She was sitting up very straight and working at the back of her hair, looking straight ahead, and I moved back a little and slipped my hand under her knees and lifted, and, as she fell back, pushed her knees up onto the couch so that she fell full length. When I went to lie down beside her, she pushed very strongly at my shoulders and said very sternly, "No! That, no!" Her anger seemed real.

"Please!" I said, and kept pressing on her shoulder as she tried to sit up. "Please, my soul!" The *"mi alma,"* a term of endearment that I had once heard Agapito use to a Spanish waitress, slipped out without my thinking, and it seemed to touch her because she stopped frowning suddenly, shook her head and laughed, and grabbed both my hands and pulled me down to her. The way she put her arms around me held me there, and I couldn't move my hands down, but her mouth seemed to be waiting for my kiss, and she did the pressing now. Her breasts, her whole body seemed to be thrusting at mine, and when her teeth opened slightly and the tip of her tongue darted out at mine, I forgot all about what I wanted to do, what I was supposed to do, and pressed my tongue against hers, and pressed and pressed, and forgot about everything, everything, except her, her, her!

Then, I could not move myself, though I wanted to get up. I felt a terrible disappointment. I knew I should have been embarrassed and ashamed, but I could not feel anything but disappointment and anger. Those thoughts about sin and immoral things were beginning to jump back at me, and I had not made it anyway. I had not done *it*. I wasn't in that world yet.

All this must have been showing in my face, because she put her arm around me and pressed me to her and patted my head. I did not care. All my excitement was gone. I thought I had failed in something.

The widow made me leave as soon as we had drunk the hot chocolate. I still did not care, then, but as soon as I was home, I began to think of her and wanted to go back. I was afraid to, and I could not go to sleep that night, I was thinking of her so much. I kept promising myself that I would see her every day now—at least until school really started. I wouldn't go swimming any more. I could do whatever I had to do in the mornings, and have all the afternoons free.

The next day I went to call on Grandfather earlier than usual. He wasn't ready to go out, but he said he would like to go for a walk and began to get ready immediately. When we came out of the park, we stopped at the widow's house, and she was waiting for us. She had on her black dress, and the coffee table was set and ready. She made no special sign to me, and of course nothing was said about my being there the day before. I thought she looked more beautiful than ever. She looked even shapelier, and her skin was lovely.

I wondered how she always seemed to be waiting for us. I wondered if Grandfather and she. . . . Why did she know when to expect us? Had Grandfather been her "lover"?—that was a hateful word to me now when it belonged to anyone else. No, I thought, No! Grandfather's too nice a man to have done a thing like that to me. While we were drinking the hot chocolate and talking, I kept watching them both to see if I could notice anything. I didn't see anything strange. I knew it was wrong and unfair to Grandfather, but I just couldn't get the thought out of my head.

Later, I ran back to the widow's house as soon as I had walked Grandfather home. I was going to ask her about it the minute I got there, I thought. I would ask her right out, say the whole thing. But when I got there she was so pleased to see me and came over to kiss me so quickly that I forgot all about the terrible idea.

We had an even nicer time than the first, but she

still held me back, though I touched her skin all over. I saw her alone every day for the next six days —I was counting them very carefully—and every time was better, and more. I was still being held back, but I knew that we were going to do it. We were getting closer to it every time.

Whenever the widow and I talked during these times we spoke of intimate things, but I never dared ask her the most important question of all—about lovers. I wasn't afraid that she might think the question too personal, because we did talk about very intimate things, but I was afraid that the answer might hurt me too much. It had to be yes, I thought, that there had been lovers. How could such a beautiful woman as the widow be alone? I knew that her husband had died many years ago.

She told me many things about her husband, and this was the way I learned one reassuring truth—that there was a nice reason for her intimacy with Grandfather. Her husband had been a commercial artist in Cuba—they had both been born and grown up there—and they had come to New York City in 1919 when he'd been offered a very good job doing layouts for a Spanish language advertising agency. Their first few months here were very happy: her husband liked the work more than he had liked his work in Cuba and the salary was double, enabling them to move much faster with their original plan of building up a big savings account that would permit the husband to take some time off to devote to his own original work, and she herself was going to a highly recommended gynecologist for treatments that might finally enable her to become pregnant.

All this luck, though, ended with the coming of winter. The misery came then, she said, using the Spanish phrase. They'd been warned about winter, which they'd never experienced before, but the humid, bitter cold of New York City was something that they had never imagined. Her husband, who had weak lungs, began to suffer constant chest colds. He stayed home a lot, sitting in the one warm room of their apartment, and trying to do his work there. She acted as a messenger between him and the agency office. She had an added bitterness of her own at this time—the gynecologist had told her that she could not conceive and he advised her to resign herself to that fact. "I could do that easily in that period," she said, "because I wanted to devote myself to my loved one. He knew this, too, I think; he was relieved when I told him the news."

She wanted to help her husband with his work, and he began to teach her the rudiments of advertising layout and design. Then, during the long hours when he was home for good, he taught her some of the intricate and technical details of the work. "He couldn't teach me inspiration," she said, "though he had so much of it himself. He had a wonderful imagination—and so much sensitivity."

She took as much of these qualities as she could absorb, and worked very hard on the technical details. She had to do this to keep up with her husband, who was working with a frenzied haste—as if he knew what was coming. He died in March, just before the April sunshine brought the first familiar warmth, and with only one day of steady hemorrhaging as a last desperate warning. The spots on his lungs that the doctors had thought were scars from an earlier attack of tuberculosis had actually included new and more virulent areas of the disease.

The tears were falling down her cheeks as she told me this, and I held her hand and pressed it. I didn't put my arm around her and draw her close to me because I felt that would offend her now. I wanted her to go on with her story, too. She was telling me these intimate things, I thought, because she wanted me to know her before she gave herself to me.

When she went on she told me how surprisingly kind everyone had been—the director of the agency and the members of the Spanish colony whom she knew only casually. It was surprising because they had been in New York City for less than a year and neither she nor her husband had made any intimate friends, but the director offered her some assignments that she could handle easily and the people of the colony were not only very attentive to her—some of them influenced the Entertainment Committee of La España into giving her the job of designing that year's fiesta program. As soon as he had met her, Don Mariano readily consented.

"I appreciated all this attention," the widow said, "much, very much, but I had to be contrary to some of it." She had had her suspicions of the agency director even before her husband had died, and when he began to invite her to dinner and then, when she had finally consented, to suggest that she take a nicer apartment in New York at his expense, she felt forced to refuse to see him socially again and, if necessary, to reject any further assignments he might give her.

At the same time, she was having the same trouble

with Don Mariano. He was a much more practical man, though, and made no suggestions about a nicer apartment. They could have a quiet affair with things just as they were, he said, and he would help her with money. She was so disgusted by this time that she turned back her assignment to the Entertainment Committee without a word of explanation, but fortunately for everybody the members knew Don Mariano and his habits quite well. They asked her to reconsider and sent Grandfather, who was Don Mariano's assistant, to deal with her.

"And that was the nicest thing of all that time," the widow said. "He was so much the gentleman, your grandfather—as he is now. He made the work pleasant but, at the same time, he consoled me. How different from those others! He consoled me for myself—not for what he might get. And I have worked for him for years, and it has never changed. It has gotten better in the best way—only that!"

She looked away but still held on to my hand. I wondered what she was thinking of, because she pressed my hand and moved it up and down gently. "How strange these things are!" she said suddenly. "If there was a man that I would have taken in those days, it would have been your grandfather—and yet he never even suggested it." She pressed my hand and looked at me. "Over the other things, he was so very much like my loved one. As you are!" she said suddenly and pulled me to her in a sudden kiss.

I put my arms around her and held the kiss, and she embraced me fiercely for a moment, but then pushed me away firmly and stood up. "You must go, now," she said. "I've talked too much."

"A little longer," I said. "Just let me stay for a few

moments." I saw that her eyes were moist, and I really wanted to stay for her sake—at least in that moment. "Don't stay alone now," I begged.

"I must," she said. She had taken my hand and was leading me to the door now. "And you must go home for dinner." She patted my cheek as we stood at the open door. "Until tomorrow, *nené!"*

"May it come soon!"

"Yes," she said.

I held the door open with my hand. She had said this yes so sincerely that I just couldn't leave. "Are you going out tonight?"

"I am—no, don't ask me with whom?"

"No, I was going to say may I wait for you later?"

She stared at me for a moment, then opened the door wider and pulled me inside by the arm. She grabbed my two arms and pushed me against the closed door. "I must be serious with you," she said sternly. "Very serious! No, don't interrupt in this moment. *Nené,* do you know that if anyone finds out about this, you will suffer. Not I. You——"

"I don't care. I love——"

"You don't know what you're saying."

"I do! I do, *mi alma,"* I said.

She shook her head but didn't say anything. She was still gripping my arms. "May God forgive me," she said in a low voice, without looking at me. Then she gripped my arms very tightly and looked at me. "I'll be home about ten," she said—in almost a sad voice, it was so serious. "No one will come in with me, but don't you come in until the car or the taxi has left the street."

"I'll be very careful. No one will see me. No one."

She shook her head again and then leaned close to me to kiss me on the lips. Then, she opened the door and really pushed me into the hall.

"No one will find out," I whispered to her just before she closed the door. "Have no worry. No one will find out."

No, I thought as I walked happily home, no one will. I had been very careful about this wonderful thing. I hadn't said a word about the widow to anybody. I was sure that even Grandfather didn't know what was going on. I had written some hints about it to my best friend who was in the country, but he wasn't a Spaniard and had nothing to do with the Spanish colony. He wouldn't talk about it anyway, I knew. Nobody had ever seen me going into the widow's house alone—I'd always looked up and down the street very carefully before I turned into it. I would be even more careful tonight; no one would see me tonight, I was sure, and tonight would be the wonderful night.

But that wasn't so—there was to be no tonight, because somebody had already found out. I didn't know it then, but I wasn't to see the widow again for a very long time. Some very important people had learned about us and were angrily talking—perhaps at that exact moment in which I had reassured her so confidently.

I never knew how it happened, but Mother or Grandmother found out, and whoever learned it first told the other immediately, because Mother was yelling at me and threatening me at the same time that Grandmother was abusing Grandfather. I learned about Grandmother later, but Mother was waiting for me at home and started yelling at me as soon as she got me alone in my room. She had closed the door, but I was sure that my brothers and sister in the front room could hear everything.

"You brute!" she kept shouting. "You little brute! How dare you! How dare you do that to that wonderful woman!" She raised her hand to slap me, but I ducked away and ran to the other side of the big bed. "What do you mean?" I said. "What do you mean?" I was really amazed at this turn of things—about the "wonderful woman," I mean. "What are you talking about?"

"You know what I mean, damn you! I can see it in your face," she said, and then she lowered her voice and went into details about what I'd done to the widow, that poor thing who couldn't slap my face because she was too nice. She sounded so full of hate with a low voice that I wished she'd kept on shouting—and some of the details were so fantastic that I'd never even dreamed of them myself.

Mother cursed me, too—but in the polite way that she always swore. "Just who the H do you think you are?" she said. "Doing a thing like that! You little S. You damned little S! Wait till I tell your father—but he'll probably think it's a joke. But just wait!"

"I didn't!" I said. "I didn't do those things!"

"You're not having supper tonight," she said as if she hadn't heard me. "And you're going to stay right here. Right in this room!" She went out and slammed the door.

She came back in less than an hour and she was dressed to go out. "Eat something in the kitchen, if you want—and then do the dishes!" she said. "Everybody's going out, but you're going to stay here. And *I* have to go to my mother's." She accented the *I*. "Your damned mess has made trouble there, too. I have to console my mother."

That was when I figured that Grandfather must have gotten some of the same treatment as I had. Poor Grandfather, I thought. Now he'll have the both of them. But I was feeling so awful myself that I could only feel sorry for him and couldn't feel that I would like to be with him so that I could help him. I didn't want to help anybody during that night.

When I did learn the truth about Grandfather later, though, I felt ashamed at being so detached from him. I felt a sudden surge of love for him because of the way he had defended me. At first I'd figured that Grandmother was railing at Grandfather because she blamed him for taking me to the widow's house in the first place, but that wasn't so. Grandfather had begun to defend me immediately, and that had made Grandmother very angry. Grandfather thought it was a quite natural thing I was doing, and he didn't see what the fuss was about. I was a young man already, Grandfather said. What did they want me to do?

I was not a young man, Grandmother had said. I was still a boy. And what they wanted me to do was to stop abusing the reputation of a respectable woman by my actions. The widow Martinez was a respectable woman, Grandmother said. Or did Grandfather have reasons for thinking otherwise?

Mother, of course, had said these same things to me. She cursed me and tried to hit me, but the thing that had made her the maddest was the fact that I was hurting a respectable woman. I didn't mind their defending the widow so strongly—how could I?—but I was surprised at the hard way they came down on Grandfather and me.

My father didn't say a word to me about it, but he did go along with Mother's idea of punishment. I had to go to my father's store every afternoon after spending the morning at home, and I wasn't allowed to go home until it was time for dinner.

During that first week I wasn't allowed out at night, but I don't think I would have tried to go to the widow's at night. I didn't know how she felt about the fuss, and I had never been there at any time but the afternoon. During the second week I was allowed to go out at night, but my mother told me that the widow's sister and niece had come to stay with her, and she hoped I wouldn't bother the poor woman any more. I went to see Grandfather one night, but he seemed very downcast. I told him how sorry I was I had spoiled our nice afternoons. He said no, it wasn't my fault and I shouldn't think that. Grandmother didn't even speak to me.

The Spanish men who worked at my father's store or came to visit there made lots of jokes about me and my "high searching." They were good-natured jokes, but nobody ever protested to my father about my punishment. The only one who ever really defended me was Grandfather. He stood up for me to Grandmother, Mother and everybody else. If it hadn't been for him, I might have really believed that I was wrong. He lost most, too, because we didn't go out for any more walks that summer, and

I always thought that that was the beginning of Grandfather's saddest time. He stayed home every day during that fall and winter, and every time I went to visit him I found him sad and not talking much.

I didn't see the widow again until the winter Spanish dance, and then she was with her sister all of the time and I couldn't speak to her alone. I met a girl in my class that winter and we began to go to the school parties together. She let me kiss her when I took her home, but it was never anything like those six days with the widow.

I was thinking of all this as I walked home that night from Grandfather's, after he had announced that he would take the chairmanship of the Entertainment Committee. I could think of it calmly now, because I knew that Grandfather was going to get over his sadness and that I was going to help him. I had been thinking about the widow a lot that winter, but I could never think of her easily because of Grandfather's getting into trouble over us. Now I knew he had a start, and I hoped he would feel as strong tomorrow. I was going to help him. I swore that to myself.

Grandfather had already written a letter when I got to his house next morning. He told me very proudly that he had gotten up at eight and gone to the corner store to make a phone call.

"I secured the number myself," he said, smiling. Grandfather had always been afraid to use the telephone because he spoke so little English. "Of course, there was no difficulty after that. I was calling *La*

*Prensa,"* he said. "I could speak Spanish immediately. I wanted the address of this man," he said, tapping the letter and nodding wisely.

Grandfather had on a white shirt and black tie and had shaved very carefully, and I thought he looked younger than I could ever remember him. He was seventy-two now, but he certainly didn't look it this morning, and he sat very straight and proud as he talked to me. I could see that he was wearing the pants of his best suit, too. I felt more reassured as I watched Grandfather. He seemed just as strong as last night.

He asked me if I would mind taking the letter home to type, instead of writing it by hand as I usually did for him.

"It's a most important letter—as you'll see," he said, handing it over to me.

"I'll be glad to type it," I said. "Of course!"

When I started to read it, my good feelings began to shiver. Grandfather was going too fast, I thought. It was a letter to the manager of Manolín, the greatest Spanish dancer in the world. Manolín had danced at the Hippodrome, the biggest theater in New York, the last time he had been in this country, and he had never come to Brooklyn. The Hippodrome had been completely filled. I remembered reading that there were people standing in the aisles, and they had had to move some of them up on the stage. Agapito was the only person we knew who had been there. Nobody like Grandfather had been able to buy a ticket, it was so expensive. No one in our family had gone. Now Grandfather was writing to the manager to ask about Manolín's fee for an appearance in Brooklyn on October 7th next, in the evening.

"I can see that you're surprised," Grandfather said. He seemed to know that I was just staring at the letter because I did not want to look at him. "It's all right, I know," Grandfather said. "It is a surprise. Your grandmother said I was crazy."

"But Manolín, Grandfather?" I looked at him.

"The first one. The best one! We should start there. I read in *La Prensa* that he was coming out of retirement, that he would start dancing in New York. It was in *La Prensa* a week ago. In the Sunday edition."

"But still?" I said. "Manolín?"

Manolín had retired four years before at the age of twenty-two, with two million dollars. He had been dancing since the age of twelve and had retired in Buenos Aires. He was supposed to have three wives there. The government was very proud to have him there, and they let him do things like that. Manolín was not a gypsy. He was from Asturias in northern Spain, where his people were miners and shepherds and had always been radicals, and he did not like to live in Spain. I had read about all this in a New York magazine.

"Notice that the manager lives in Peekskill right now," Grandfather was saying. "We could take a trip up there if there were need of it." Grandfather was very hearty and sure. He spoke very confidently. He seemed to have brushed aside my surprise. "Yes, that would be a nice trip," he said.

Later, when I came back with the letter typed, Grandfather read it very carefully and then signed it slowly.

"I know it's correct," he said, "because you are a very good scholar."

"It was correct before, Grandfather," I said. This

was true. Grandfather wrote very simply but very correctly. "It was a good letter. The only thing I worry about is will it do any good."

"We can only try," Grandfather said, but his confident face didn't have the look of trying. He had sealed the letter and now brought out his wallet and took two stamps out. One was a Special Delivery stamp. This was only the second time that I had seen one used, and I was even more surprised at Grandfather.

"Is it necessary to write anything on the envelope about this?" he said as he pasted the big stamp on.

"I don't think so," I said, but just to be sure I printed "Special Delivery" on the envelope.

Grandfather mailed the letter with a flourish. He asked me to tell him how soon it would be picked up, and I was happy to see on the chart that it would be picked up in forty-seven minutes. Grandfather shook my hand as we stood by his door.

"We won't say anything about this to anyone, we two," he said. I shook my head. "This is a thing that should be known slowly."

"Yes," I said eagerly. "Because then if nothing happens, it won't be so bad."

"Oh, no!" Grandfather said. "Nothing like that. I mean it to be known, and Grandmother will certainly tell many people. I would prefer it to be slowly, and not from us. That's all. And something will happen, young one! I know that."

"Yes, Grandfather," I said.

"Now, will you call for me at two o'clock? We must go to the printer's. And to other places."

I learned what Grandfather meant by "other places" that afternoon. We went to the printer's for just a routine visit, and I kept wondering why Grandfather had wanted me along and why he was wearing his best suit. Then we went straight to the widow Martinez's from there. It was a wonderful surprise to me, and it was a surprise to the widow. She was dressed and greeted us warmly, but she said something very quietly about having lost the hope of enjoying visits from us again. Grandfather explained that he had taken over the executive duties of the Entertainment Committee and that he wanted her to design the program as she had done so beautifully many years before. The widow blushed—it was thrilling to see that again—and said that for a gentleman like Grandfather she would be only too happy to do it. I remembered what she had told me about Don Mariano and the sudden memory of it—coming so soon after the pleasant shock of seeing the widow again—made me very mad, but it was a pleasant mad because she was safe with us here now.

We had hot chocolate in the same happy way as the year before, and then we left. Grandfather said on the street that the widow's sister and niece were still living with her, but that they would be leaving very soon. He patted my shoulder. I felt very happy, and just as confident as he.

I thought the widow had looked more beautiful than ever because she seemed strangely sad and a little older, and I felt now that she needed me. I wanted her more than before, but it didn't seem like a thing of mine alone now because she, too, had a need of someone, and I felt more confident about it. I felt I could even wait calmly until her sister and niece went away.

Mother didn't ask where Grandfather and I had

been, but that night I heard her talking to Father about "the Manolín business." Father said he'd heard all about it and that the men had been talking about it at the store. The old man was mad, Father said, and Mother answered him very quickly. "And don't forget," she said, "he's still my father." I was glad to hear her say that. She wouldn't be bothering me about anything now while I was working with Grandfather. The last thing Father said was that she shouldn't be getting so excited because the letter to Manolín's manager wouldn't be answered anyway, and then Grandfather would give up his foolishness.

But the letter was answered right away. The answer came in two days, which meant the manager had sat down to write it as soon as he read our letter, and he had sent it by special delivery. Grandfather rushed over with the letter in the morning. He had been able to read it easily because it was written in Spanish, but he wanted me to know right away. He was so excited that he hadn't bothered to shave or dress up. The letter said that the manager was going to be in New York that weekend and that we should come to see him any time after two o'clock at the Hotel Waldorf-Astoria in Suite 1002.

I was surprised at the letter—not because it had come so quickly or because of what it said—but because it was written in the same old-fashioned script and had the same spelling mistakes and run-together of words as Grandfather's letters from his sister in the little *pueblo* in Spain, and I thought that the manager of a rich, famous man like Manolín should have a very good secretary, or should be able to write better than that himself. I was reassured by the fact that the manager was staying at the Waldorf-Astoria, but then I thought that he might just be faking that, and that maybe he was a servant to somebody who had that suite. Of course, I didn't say anything about this to Grandfather—he was so happy and pleased—and I tried to keep smiling and nodding my head.

That Saturday we took the el to the city at one o'clock, just to give ourselves plenty of time. Grandfather did not like the el—he was a little afraid of it —but he took it today in deference to me.

"And if I were ten years younger," he said, "we would have taken the Subterranean. Yes!"

The Subterranean was the subway, and I said, "Oh, no. This is fine!" to reassure Grandfather, and did not tell him that I had ridden on the el and the subway so much in the time we'd been separated that I was already bored with them.

Grandfather seemed a little doubtful this afternoon, and I tried to keep him talking about his life in Spain and Morocco so that he wouldn't think about the manager and the interview. I didn't feel so confident myself, but I hated to see Grandfather lose any of that wonderful feeling he had these days.

I was asking him to tell me about the time he was a waiter in the best hotel in Tangier, and I was thinking about that strange, poor letter of the manager's, and how it would be if he wasn't really living at the Waldorf-Astoria but would meet us in the lobby and then take us to the hotel he really lived in, a dirty, dusty hotel that would make Grandfather feel ashamed. I just couldn't forget that letter. I wondered how I would manage to cheer up Grandfather later.

When we got to the hotel and walked through that wonderful lobby to the desk and they knew the manager's name right away and sent us up to his suite, I began to feel very reassured. It was a wonderful hotel, and everything looked very rich. Grandfather was smiling as we went up in the elevator.

The man who answered our knock looked just like a photograph of a Spanish peasant. He was an old man with a bright, clean hard face that was well sunned. He had on a beret, a blue shirt open at the neck, and his neat black pants were held up by a sash. He wore *alpargatas,* those rope-soled black slippers that I had seen in so many pictures of Spanish people.

"Señor Figueira!" he said in a hoarse voice—that was his natural voice, I saw later—and shook hands with Grandfather and then with me as he waved us into the room. "Señor Gomez to serve you," he said.

That was the manager's name, and so he was Manolín's manager. I still couldn't believe it, because he looked so nice and natural, just like an old Spanish peasant, and I had had a very different idea of how the manager of Manolín was supposed to look. But this Mr. Gomez acted just as if he belonged here, pointing out chairs to us and then going over to a bureau that had a lot of liquor bottles on it. He held one up to Grandfather and said, *"Jerez?"* He had a really harsh, raucous voice, but he looked like a nice simple old man, even though he didn't smile much.

"With much pleasure!" Grandfather said and nodded, and Mr. Gomez poured out three glasses. The one he gave me had a little less in it, but it was the same kind as theirs.

"This one is my grandson," Grandfather said as

Mr. Gomez sat down with us. "Born here, but very Spanish."

"That's the way!" Mr. Gomez said. He made a fist at me. *"Así, así!"* I was surprised at how strongly he said it.

He held out his glass and clicked it with Grandfather's and then with mine, and we each took a sip. Mr. Gomez nodded at Grandfather and then drank off his sherry in one swallow. Grandfather did the same. Mr. Gomez wiped the back of his hand across his mouth, but Grandfather took out his pocket handkerchief and neatly touched his mouth. I could tell Grandfather was very nervous, but he was dignified as ever. I felt proud of him. I thought he belonged in this rich, wonderful room with its thick carpet and big chairs much more than Mr. Gomez did, even though Mr. Gomez was such a nice, natural man.

Mr. Gomez had gone back to the bureau. He put his empty glass on top of it and took a batch of papers out of the top drawer. As he came back to us, he was pulling one of them out of the pack. He sat down again and opened the paper and handed it to Grandfather. Grandfather put on his glasses, and as soon as he'd begun to read the paper his face changed. He smiled when he looked up and nodded at Mr. Gomez, but I could see that the paper worried him.

Mr. Gomez pulled out another and handed it to Grandfather before he had finished the first. When Grandfather began to read this one, his face got even more worried and strained, but he still smiled and nodded to Mr. Gomez when he looked up.

"Two thousand dollars for one, and fifteen hundred for another." Grandfather's voice was very quiet. "I congratulate you, though it is well deserved."

Mr. Gomez took the paper from Grandfather's hand. "I have seven contracts like these," he said, as he put the two papers back into the pile. "From New York to San Francisco." He pronounced this just like a Spaniard, and looked at Grandfather. "I show them to you because I know you can't afford payments like that."

Grandfather shook his head slowly. I thought how terribly disappointed he must feel. Fifteen hundred dollars! La España couldn't afford anything like that. The most they had ever paid was five hundred dollars. Fifteen hundred and two thousand dollars—that was surely the end of the Manolín dream for us. Still, I had to admire how well Grandfather was taking it. He didn't act as if it was the end of everything. He kept his dignity, no matter how much it cost him. He had reached into his pocket and brought out a pack of cigars and held them up to Mr. Gomez. Grandfather had even remembered that little courtesy.

Mr. Gomez took one of the cigars and passed it under his nose admiringly. He looked at the pack again and, when Grandfather smiled and nodded, he took another one.

"These are luxuries for me still," Mr. Gomez said. "Many thanks."

They were luxuries for Grandfather too, I knew—real luxuries, not "said" ones—but you'd never think it to see the easy, dignified way he'd offered them.

"As I was saying," Mr. Gomez said. He pointed one of the cigars at Grandfather. "I know you can't afford these fees," he said. Why does he keep rubbing it in? I thought. Why doesn't he just end it nicely, the way Grandfather is trying to do? "But what can you afford?" Mr. Gomez said. "How much can you afford?"

Grandfather shrugged his shoulders. "Two hundred and fifty dollars. I hesitate to tell you this. At the most, three hundred dollars."

"Two hundred and fifty dollars would be better?"

"I regret to say yes. Even that!"

"All right." Mr. Gomez pointed the cigar again. "Good, then! For two hundred and fifty dollars. Manolín. One night in Brooklyn."

Grandfather had started to shrug his shoulders. He stopped short and stared at Mr. Gomez. I had been sipping my drink, and I heard my teeth click suddenly on the glass. All right! he had said.

"Do I understand you correctly?" Grandfather said. "We can obtain Manolín for two hundred and fifty dollars?"

"You understand me correctly," Mr. Gomez said. "Yes! October the seventh, you said." He closed his eyes for a moment. "A night of Saturday," he said slowly, as if he had not yet finished figuring. "Saturday."

"The night of Saturday," Grandfather said, nodding. "In Brooklyn. Yes!" Grandfather's face had brightened and he was leaning forward. "We have not hired the hall, definitely, but we will do that immediately."

"I advise you," Mr. Gomez said, pointing the cigar

again. "I will tell other managers that this is a tryout, a test. To explain the big difference in fees. As for you and me, we know that Manolín is Manolín. This may be a tryout because it is the first time in a long time —but it will be no different than when Manolín begins officially in Chicago."

"I understand," Grandfather said. He nodded solemnly. "The first time for Manolín is a double honor for us. We have much to thank you for, Señor Gomez."

"For nothing," Mr. Gomez said. He waved the cigar. "They're not deserved. I knew that I was going to let you have Manolín the moment you came in. I liked you. You looked like one of us. I want Manolín to start among his likes—Spaniards like you and me —and a little group." He waved the cigar as Grandfather started to protest. "I know you'll have many, and you can advertise as much as you want. All that! But still, I know it will be a little group around him, Manolín, a little group of Spaniards. Understand?"

"Yes, and it shall be like that. I can assure you of it," Grandfather said. They shook hands very warmly.

We took the subway home. It was a long ride, but it seemed to go very fast. Grandfather enjoyed it very much. He talked all during the ride. Then, when we walked home from the subway station, he smoked one of his cigars even though he wasn't supposed to. The doctor had made him stop smoking years ago.

Grandfather had a right to brag about getting Manolín, but I never realized the news would travel so fast. My mother knew about it even before I reached our house, and I missed the chance of getting to tell her and of watching her surprise. Still, she certainly was surprised. I knew, because she was very quiet about it. She just asked me if it was true.

"Yes," I said.

"And it's going to be all right?" she said.

"Of course!" I said, even though I wondered why she should ask like that.

When my father came home late from the store, he said all the men had been talking about it. "I've been hearing nothing but 'Manolín' all night," I heard him say to my mother. "Is it true?"

"Of course it's true," my mother said sharply. "The boy was with him."

My father said something I couldn't hear, and then I heard my mother call me. "Are you awake?" she said.

I said yes and she came into our room, with my father following her. When she turned and said, "Well?" to my father she said it very low because my brother was sound asleep.

"Did you see the manager?" my father asked me. "The manager of Manolín?"

"Mr. Gomez. Yes," I said.

"He's the manager of Manolín, the great dancer?"

"Yes," I said. "You should have seen the place he had. In the Waldorf-Astoria."

"And everything was arranged? Definitely?"

"Yes. I'm going to take the contract to him to sign Monday. Grandfather and I are going to copy it from a form tomorrow. I'm going to type it out."

"I see," my father said. He nodded. He turned to go when Mother pushed at his arm.

"All right," she said to me. "Now go to sleep."

She started to talk to my father as soon as they were out of the room. "Just because it's my father," I heard her saying, "you don't believe it. Isn't that it?" She sounded very strong, but I remembered how quiet she had been about it that afternoon.

Whatever it was for anybody else, it was a great triumph for Grandfather. Sunday afternoon, the next day, as soon as I'd finished eating, I went over to Grandfather's and we went down to the La España headquarters to get the contract form. People had been at Grandfather's to ask if it was true about Manolín and then to congratulate him, and when we got to the La España headquarters the card room was filled with men. They crowded around Grandfather as soon as he came in, asking and congratulating again. Grandfather looked taller than anybody—he was dressed in his best suit and a clean white shirt and black tie—and he was still very dignified, in spite of being so happy. He had to drink some part of four whiskeys even though he wasn't supposed to drink anything but wine. They were all bought for him, and Grandfather sipped at them expertly in toasts. Then he could leave the rest because the very efficient bartender quietly slipped away the unfinished glass without anyone noticing, and set up a new one.

When we left and were out in the street, walking toward the trolley, Grandfather took my hand and pressed it. I saw that he was smiling and shaking his head.

"Did you notice, young one?" he said. "Did you notice how frightened they seem? All of them?"

"Yes! Yes, Grandfather." I was so glad he'd noticed. "They seem frightened—all of them. And yesterday it was Mother and Father. The same thing."

"Yes." Grandfather stopped smiling, but was still shaking his head in an unbelieving way. "They're fearful. As if it's too much! As if it's too much that we've got Manolín. I am fearful many times. But before a thing happens. When something that is dangerous or terrible is coming, then I am afraid. I admit such fears. But not after the thing happens. Not when the thing is settled and done, and we have won. What we fear has not happened—what we wanted has been done. Manolín is coming to our fiesta. It's settled. We have nothing to be frightened of now. The good is coming. What we needed and wanted we got! Do you see?" He pressed my hand and looked at me. "*You* do see, I know. You see what I'm telling you. Thee, my one true disciple." Grandfather laughed suddenly and pinched my cheek. "I am giving myself too much importance."

"No, Grandfather! No, you're not!" I wanted to tell him how much I *did* see. "You're not doing that —not giving yourself too much importance." He was better than all of us, I thought, because I was getting a little worried about all this fear business, too. "You did this yourself, and you're doing the rest, too. They're afraid of it, but you're not. You got Manolín, and you know it. They don't! Mother and Father were afraid last night, and now all these people, too. I'm glad you're not afraid. I don't want to be afraid, either."

*"Hombre!"* Grandfather patted my cheek again. "Thee, afraid!"

"No. Because you're not."

I'd been so worried that Grandfather would notice all that fear around us even before I had—and he'd laughed at it.

"No, Grandfather," I said. "No, I'm not afraid."

Typing up the contract was a simple job. I just copied the form from the year before and made the right changes. The last year's entertainment fee was three hundred dollars, and the singer used wasn't anywhere near the great Manolín's class. Grandfather and I looked at each other and laughed when we came to that point.

We were sitting in our parlor, with the typewriter on the center table. Mother had been very nice when we came in and had insisted we work in the best room. She was still very quiet but she treated Grandfather respectfully. She had kissed his hand when he first came in, and not his cheek as she usually did. Grandfather had smiled and kissed her on the cheek. He winked at me slyly as we went into the parlor.

After I finished two copies of the contract, Grandfather signed them and showed me where Manolín's manager was to sign. Then I typed out the check for the fee and Grandfather signed this with a flourish. I couldn't blame him. We put the contracts and the check in an envelope and put it in the inside pocket of my jacket, all ready to take to New York the next day. I should have felt nervous that night, with the jacket hanging in my room and all this being so important, but I slept deeply and well.

I took the subway to New York early the next morning, before I went to school to register, and I met Mr. Gomez again at the Waldorf-Astoria. He was just the same—he was clean and bright, and with the same clothes. He still looked like a nice simple Spanish peasant, but I didn't worry about that anymore. He signed the two contracts and kept one copy and the check. When he asked me if I'd like a drink, I said, "Oh, no! Not now," and he laughed. Then he asked me how the people of La España felt about Manolín coming to the fiesta, and I told him what a sensation the news had been, without mentioning the fear of so many La España members that it was all too good to be true.

"The old one's had a triumph, eh?" he said.

"Grandfather? Yes, a real one. A very real one."

"I like that man," he said. "I like him. I move by feelings, and I liked him as soon as I saw him."

"He's a wonderful man."

"Yes," he said. "He is." He put his hand on my shoulder as we walked toward the door. "We were lucky to have met, young one," he said. "Your grandfather gets Manolín very cheaply. We get a lucky place to start. I feel it's very fortunate. Manolín will begin well." He patted my shoulder and reached out to shake my hand. "And just remember this, young one," he said. "Manolín is Manolín, no matter what happens. Remember that!" He looked at me very seriously as he said this. "Manolín is Manolín—in all ways and any way."

"Oh, surely," I said. "Surely. We know that."

He nodded. "Good!" he said.

I was surprised at the strong way he'd said this last thing, and I was thinking about it as I walked to the elevator. I couldn't figure it out and I was a little worried about it, but I never realized for a moment that it was a terrible warning.

Manolín's ship from Buenos Aires came in to New York that Thursday afternoon. Mr. Gomez had called the La España headquarters to tell Grandfather, but Grandfather wasn't there and Mr. Gomez had left the message. That way the news got around fast, and practically everybody we knew was planning to go down to the pier to meet the ship. It was as if they really believed, at last, that Manolín was coming to La España and wanted to see him in person in order to keep that belief alive. Even Mother was planning to go now—my brothers and sister would be in school—but she decided against it when she found that Grandmother wasn't going, and decided to stay with her. It wasn't that Grandmother thought she would be too nervous; she just didn't want to see the excitement. I felt secretly glad that Grandmother wasn't going. Grandfather wouldn't feel right if she were there. And when Thursday afternoon came and turned out the way it did, I was very, very glad that Grandmother wasn't there.

I cut a class to get to the pier on time. It was only a gym class and Grandfather had said that this was okay. He said he wanted me surely to be there. I arrived just in time, but I didn't mind. Practically the whole Spanish colony from Brooklyn was there, and I was glad that I didn't get called to talk to anybody. I saw my two aunts, my uncles, Agapito and a lot of others I knew, but I didn't have to stop to talk because the ship had already docked and the gangplank put in place, and they were all standing around the foot of the gangplank and looking up at the group of passengers getting ready to come off.

I went around to the edge of the crowd and found

a spot near the rail where I could see the whole gangplank clearly. I could see Grandfather, too, standing next to Mr. Gomez just near the foot of the gangplank. Agapito was standing near them and he was dressed in his best bright clothes. He stood out, but he couldn't take anything from Grandfather who looked tall and dignified and noble in his black suit and hat. Mr. Gomez was still dressed as he had been at the hotel, except that he had on the jacket of a black suit. He still wore his beret.

The first of the passengers had begun to come down, and I looked up at the group that was standing around the head of the gangplank. A man with a woman on his arm and another woman coming right behind them moved into this group along the ship's deck, and my heart suddenly began to beat faster. I don't know why, but I felt instinctively that this was Manolín. The man and the two women were laughing and talking, and my heart kept racing as I watched them. I turned quickly to look at Mr. Gomez to see if he was looking up toward this man, and when I saw that he was looking straight at the man and that his old face was stern and hard, I suddenly remembered his terrible warning at the hotel as he was saying good-by to me: "Remember this, young one. Manolín is Manolín, no matter what happens!" No, I thought. Oh, no! Don't let this be Manolín! Please! Then Mr. Gomez raised his hand in a slight, almost embarrassed wave, and the man with the two women, who was standing beside the officers now, lifted his head and smiled down at Mr. Gomez.

I began to feel sick. My heart thumped. It was cool, but I began to feel the sweat trickle down my side. I stared at the man at the head of the gangplank as he smiled and shook hands with the officers. I couldn't believe it. No! I turned to stare at Mr. Gomez. He was standing rigidly but hunched up, with his hands in his jacket pockets. Grandfather was looking calmly up at the gangplank, and most of the other people were talking among themselves. Nobody seemed to be giving any attention to the man at the head of the gangplank. Nobody seemed to realize that this was Manolín. Even when Mr. Gomez took a short, tight step forward to stand near the foot of the gangplank, nobody moved with him. They paid little attention to the man who had started to walk down the gangplank with the girl still hanging onto his arm, and I could understand why. I could understand it with a sickening realization, because the man coming down the gangplank was the biggest, fattest man I'd ever seen in all my life.

He not only looked that way, but he seemed to have done everything to make it worse. He wore a heavy, fluffy coat that reached past his knees and made his body look huge, and he had a small, pancake beret set tight on his head to make it look even smaller than it seemed. And he had no dignity. The girl hanging on his arm was very small, but she seemed to upset his balance and he held tightly to the gangplank rail with his free hand as he waddled down in long, crazy, heel-first steps. That might have been due to the stepping boards on the gangplank, but I couldn't think of any excuse as I watched Manolín come down the gangplank. No single thing could explain the way he looked now.

He was laughing all the time and talking back to

the girl, and his long black hair was pushing out under the tight beret, and he looked crazy as he moved like that. He looked crazy and horrible. I turned to watch Grandfather, and saw Mr. Gomez turn and talk to him when Manolín was halfway down the gangplank. Grandfather stepped forward beside him. For a moment he had hesitated, and his face had changed in the way it did when he was suddenly frightened or sad, but he lifted his head and pushed his shoulders back as he stood beside Mr. Gomez. He was tall and erect, and Mr. Gomez seemed to get tighter and smaller.

Even there, I thought, Grandfather had most to lose, and yet he took it better than anybody. For when the hulking, laughing lump finally reached the foot of the gangplank and embraced Mr. Gomez in a bear hug and shook hands with Grandfather, the people all around suddenly realized that this must be Manolín and they just stopped everything and stood there looking, with their mouths open. Then first Agapito, and all the men after him, put on big polite smiles, and nodded and smiled, and came up to shake hands with the great Manolín. Then the ladies were brought up to be introduced to him. Manolín seemed to make a great show of this, but I couldn't stand any more of it and as the crowd gathered into a group around him I walked over to the other side of the pier and waited.

At the end, I went home with Grandfather in a taxi. My youngest aunt, Elvira, had come over to me and made me promise to take Grandfather home in a taxi. She gave me the money.

"Now, stay with Grandfather!" she said. "All the

time. This is a terrible thing, so stay with him."

"Grandfather'll be all right," I said. "You don't have to worry about him."

"I do. This is a terrible thing. I want you to stay with him."

"I'll stay with him," I said. "Don't worry." A lot you know, I thought.

I guess the original plan was for Grandfather and some of the men to go to the hotel with Manolín, but Manolín and his party went alone with Mr. Gomez. Nobody came with Grandfather and me, either. Most of the men were embarrassed, and they laughed a lot. It was just like them, I thought. First they were fearful, then they were laughing like fools, and they didn't know the truth either time.

Grandfather and I didn't say much in the taxi. It was only the third time I'd ever been in a taxi, but I couldn't enjoy it. I thought of the nice long ride to Brooklyn as a bad thing, not as a thrilling one. Grandfather sat in the corner with his head held up, but I could tell he wasn't looking at anything. When we were going over the Brooklyn Bridge, I felt so mad about not being able to enjoy it that I just had to curse. "That damned Mr. Gomez!"

*"Hombre!"* Grandfather said. He leaned over and put his hand on my arm. *"Poor* Mr. Gomez! He felt this as much as we. As much!"

"How could he?"

"He did," Grandfather said. He patted my arm. "He did. I know."

Grandfather watched me for a moment, and when I didn't say anything he leaned back and just stared out. I didn't say anything more during the whole trip. When we got home, Grandmother seemed to know everything, but she didn't say a word about Manolín. She talked only a little, and I thought she wasn't as cold as usual to Grandfather.

When the three of us were eating dinner very quietly, Grandmother suddenly said, "Let's stop thinking about it, yes? It was a contract for Manolín, and it's Manolín, no matter how. Isn't that so?" she said to Grandfather.

"Exactly," he said. "Exactly. Manolín it is, and Manolín it will be."

"And you'll go through with it?"

"Yes." Grandfather held his head up and looked at her very seriously. "Yes, I will."

"Good, then," she said. "We'll stop thinking about it."

For the rest of the meal, we talked about ships. After dinner Grandfather and I went into the front parlor. I thought he was just going to sit there quietly, but he went to the big table and took a large envelope out of the drawer.

"You must go on an errand for us," he said, bringing it over to me.

"No, Grandfather, I want to stay with you."

"But, young one, why?"

"Well, this thing that happened today. I know how you feel about it."

"I feel as you do, but we must go on. We must go all the way. Your grandmother said it—it is still Manolín."

"You don't believe that," I said, "do you?" I had been thinking this all afternoon, but hadn't wanted to say it. "You don't."

"No. I don't believe it. We can't believe it, you nor I. We hoped for so much, and knew what we wanted." Grandfather patted my cheek and I felt I was going to cry. "But we must act as if we do believe it," he said, holding my chin and looking at me very sternly. "We were the brave ones before. We must be much more now. Thou and I," he said, with the familiar "thou." "The good pair!"

When I tried to nod against his hand, he smiled and slapped my cheek lightly. I could see how much it cost him to smile and how sad the rest of his face was.

The envelope Grandfather gave me contained the proofs of the program cover, and I was to take them to the widow, but even that fact couldn't make me feel any better. As I walked to her house the streets were dark and quiet, but I could feel no confidence. I knew I wouldn't meet any friend and I had a right to go to her house, but I couldn't feel anything about it. I kept remembering Grandfather's face and Manolín's fat body coming down the gangplank. Nothing seemed to matter after that.

I couldn't remember whether the widow's sister and niece were still living with her, but I knew I wouldn't care if they were still there. It would be better if they were—things would be quicker and easier then.

I must have walked slowly, because the widow's street was dark and quiet when I reached there and it seemed very late. There was no light in the widow's front room, but I went into the hallway and rang the bell of her apartment anyway. The widow herself opened the door almost immediately. She opened it a little at first, saying, "Who is it? Who?" and then opened it wide when she saw it was me, and said, "Come in. Come in, *hijo*."

She had on a dark dressing gown, and her hair was set in a braid that was wound around her head like a small halo.

"I was just going to bed," she said, when she saw me looking at it. "I didn't think anyone would come tonight, anyone—and I would have understood."

"Because of this afternoon?"

"Yes. You, poor thing!" She patted my cheek. "And the poor old one! How I felt for him when I heard. Please sit down. Please sit down," she said.

I had been standing by the sofa, and she took my arm and pushed me back gently. When I put the envelope and my hat beside me, she picked them up.

"Are these the proofs of the program?" she said.

"Yes."

She had turned and placed them on the bureau and was moving over to shut the bedroom door.

"Are you alone?" I said. I wanted her to stop moving around and come over and sit down beside me. I wanted to put my arms around her and hug her tightly, and put my face into that wonderful big bosom and cry.

"You mean have my sister and niece gone?" She turned to look at me with her hand still on the doorknob, and she stared at me so long that I blushed and looked down.

"Yes, that's what I mean," I said. "Yes."

"Yes, I am alone," she said. She had started to walk

toward the kitchen, but when I looked at her she came over suddenly and sat beside me. She lifted my chin and stared at me, then put her arms around me and pressed me to her. I kissed her cheek. When she turned to me, I kissed her on the mouth.

"You had forgotten that, I thought," she said very seriously. "You had forgotten all that."

"I never did. I thought of it all the time," I said. "All the time, all through the year."

She kissed me and pressed me very close. "And now, that of this afternoon happens. Poor *hijo!*" she said. "Poor little one."

"Don't think of this afternoon," I said. "Don't think of it." I didn't want to think of this afternoon now. I didn't feel like crying, either. I wanted to hold her. Everything of this afternoon, everything of the past year seemed to go away. I remembered the last time we had been on this couch. I remembered that clearly, and this seemed to be the next time that was coming right after. "Don't think of this afternoon," I said, trying to work my arms out of her embrace. "Don't think of it." The only one I cared about in this afternoon's business was Grandfather, and he knew that I was here.

I slipped my arm out and put it around her and then reached inside her gown with my other hand, but she grabbed my arms tightly and pushed me back.

"Please," I said. "I don't want to think of this afternoon. I want to——"

"I know what you want," she said. She lifted my face and made me look at her. "Are you serious, *niño?* Are you serious in this?"

"Oh, yes! Yes, I am. And not afraid anymore—no matter what anyone says!"

"Good, then." She looked at me for a moment, then kissed me lightly on the lips and stood up. She pulled me up by the hand and pointed to the bedroom door. "Go in there. Take off your jacket, first," she said. When I just stood staring at her, she reached over to help me. "Take off the rest in there," she said. Her face was very determined-looking.

When I went into the room, the light by the bed was still on. The sheets were turned down, but the bed had not been slept in. I was suddenly frightened and lonely, but I began to take off my clothes because of the determined way she had said it. I kept on my shorts until I was under the covers, and then took them off and threw them on the chair with my other clothes. I heard her putting the latch on the front door, and then she came into the room. She walked directly to the lamp and went to put it out. "No!" I said. "Please don't." I reached out my hand. She shook her head at me and smiled, but left the light on.

I thought she would take off her robe then, but she knelt down by the side of the bed. She made the sign of the cross and bent her head to pray. I was so shocked that I forgot my fright and embarrassment. I even lost the memory of the afternoon, and I kept my eyes down so I couldn't look at her. I would never forget this moment, I thought, I would never forget it. But I did.

As soon as she stood up and took off her robe—she had nothing on underneath—and I saw how full and beautiful she was, I forgot all about the praying and all about everything else. I didn't care how frightened I was; I reached out for her even before she came into the bed. I was talking to her. I was calling her by her first name. I knew I would never *forget* these next moments of my life, these next hours. Never. As long as I lived. Never, never, never.

Mother didn't say anything when I got home very late that night, and I'd almost forgotten the reason why—the tragedy of the afternoon. The next morning though, when I woke up and remembered the widow, I felt so grateful to Grandfather for having sent me that I made a silent promise to help him as much as I could. If he wanted to see this through, I would stay with him all the way.

During my first class, I kept thinking of ideas that would help Grandfather. I thought of a lot of crazy ones, but no practical ones. I tried not to think of the widow while I was working for Grandfather, but she stayed in my mind all the time and, toward the end of the period, I began to think of nothing but her. At the first recess, I told my best friend all about the night before. I tried not to brag or make it too good because I knew that he had never had a woman and would feel hurt, but I couldn't help bringing in some of the wonderful things. Charlie thought I was lying and said it didn't show. I tried to convince him, but I was certainly glad if it was true that it didn't show.

When I went to La España headquarters to see Grandfather, I didn't have to worry whether it showed or not, because Grandfather was very depressed and I knew he wouldn't notice. I began to feel sad myself and started to talk about something to make him feel better, but Grandfather stopped me.

"No," he said, "you don't have to do that. It's all right for me to be depressed in front of you. Either of us can be depressed before the other, but we mustn't show it outside."

He told me that Mr. Gomez had been to see him early that morning and had offered to drop the contract and return the fee. Mr. Gomez had explained to Grandfather that he had feared such a disaster as the one they were in now but that he had not warned Grandfather for two reasons. One was that he had hoped it would not be so bad, that Manolín would not be so fat; the other was that he still believed Manolín to be Manolín—the greatest Spanish dancer in the world. He was convinced of that, no matter what.

Mr. Gomez had also said that he'd taken a suite in a downtown Brooklyn hotel for Manolín and his party, as well as for himself. He said that Manolín would begin a training routine the next day by walking or running around Prospect Park, the biggest park in Brooklyn. "I want him to keep mobility," Mr. Gomez had said. "It's the only thing I truly worry about."

"I told him that routine would only tire him," Grandfather said. He shook his head sadly.

"What did you say about the contract, Grandfather? What about that?"

"I told him no," Grandfather said. He looked at me and patted my cheek. "No!" Grandfather stood up and began to walk around. "You know how I feel about religion and God, young one," he said. "I have no orthodox beliefs. I go to Mass once in so often to please your grandmother." He kept clapping and rubbing his hands together as he talked. "But I believe there's a God of something somewhere. We get a touch of Him sometimes, this God, if we're very, very lucky. At some rare, rare time. I thought it was here for me at this time. I took the executive position because I had a feeling of something good, and then when we got Manolín I was almost very sure of it. Now, it seems to be going wrong, but I can't surrender it. I don't want to. I don't think it started for me to turn out disgraced, to become a fool. That couldn't be a touch of God. It has to be something important—no matter how it works itself. That's why I want to hold it. I want to stay with it. *Niño,*" he said, stopping in front of me, "you don't have to understand this—just feel it. One can do nothing else. Just feel it."

"Oh, I feel it," I said. "I feel it, Grandfather. And I understand some of it." I had never heard Grandfather or anybody else in my family talk so personally of God. This was the way some of my high-school teachers talked about God and religion, and it seemed to me a new and thrilling way to think of God. I had never thought that Grandfather would talk of God like that. "I understand some of it," I said again. "Yes, I do, Grandfather."

"And you want me to go on? You know I have to?"

"Yes, Grandfather, I do. I would have said yes to Mr. Gomez to break the contract, but I'm glad you didn't."

Grandfather patted my cheek. "You must stay with me in your thinking. All the way," he said.

I left the La España headquarters early, so that I

could get my homework done and go to the widow's that night for the corrected proofs. While I was working I couldn't help thinking of Grandfather's suddenly talking about God like that. I felt sure now that he was becoming a great man. This business of Manolín was making him the kind of man that a teacher of a famous prodigy is, and I felt glad that Grandfather was so strong because he was bringing me along with him in this thing and making me feel different. I began to worry about what I was going to do at the widow's tonight. It didn't seem right now. I knew it wasn't a sin, but it didn't seem right. I felt guilty about having so much pleasure while Grandfather had none.

I didn't want to spoil the good feeling Grandfather had given me this afternoon, but when I got to the widow's and saw her—how beautiful she was and how close to me and to us—I felt that it couldn't be wrong because she belonged in this wonderful feeling. She was a part, with Grandfather and me. I was the lucky one to get the benefits from her, but she was a definite part of this new feeling that we had.

That was just two weeks before the fiesta. Manolín would dance for La España just two weeks from that Saturday. I was able to keep my good feeling through all that time because of the widow. I saw her every night. She was the only thing that reminded me of how I should feel. She kept the feeling alive. I would be with Grandfather and see his great worry; I would feel that we were all going down, that two weeks from now we would all be done with, Grandfather, the widow and I. Then I would be with her—she was so alive to me, the most intimate person I had ever known, that I felt we could not be stopped, we could not be done with. I always kept some of her feeling to take to Grandfather the next day.

During those two weeks I spent more time with Grandfather than with the widow. He needed me much more. I knew he still held that small core of hope for something good, but I saw very little sign of it. Grandfather tried to keep up a front before others, but with me he was truthful and depressed and gray. He shaved every morning, but his face began to have a gray, mournful look.

I know that he fainted on Tuesday of the second week, but fortunately only Jacobo was in the headquarters at the time, and he was a sharp, taciturn old man who wouldn't say a word. He told only me —for Grandfather's protection, as he said—and I didn't tell anyone. I was afraid, but I knew that Grandfather wouldn't want anyone in the colony to know about it—certainly not the family. I asked Grandfather if it wouldn't be a good thing to go to a doctor—just he and I alone, without anyone else knowing about it—but he said no. He would go later. He had had a weak heart before, and he still had some medicine that the doctor had given him years ago. He would take that, he said.

"I can suffer through this, young one," he said. "Don't worry."

That was a good word that Grandfather used—suffer. That's just what he was doing. He was taking the whole weight of this possible tragedy alone. I don't think I was doing much by just being with him, and the rest of the colony was leaving him alone.

Even the members of the Entertainment Committee only met with him once during those two weeks, and that was just a formal meeting for the final fiesta arrangements. The Spanish colony seemed to feel that Grandfather was just being stubborn about the Manolín business, and they were going to let him be stuck with it. Grandfather had always had a reputation for being stubborn.

There were some rare exceptions among the people, but they were not surprising ones. Agapito, for instance, was a helpful friend. When the Lyceum was sold out, he secured a bigger hall for the same price, and he gave Grandfather much practical advice. Old Jacobo was also a good friend. He couldn't do much, but he stayed around headquarters a good deal.

The fact that the first stock of tickets had been sold out immediately and that requests were coming from as far as Chicago should have been a wonderful thing for the fiesta, but it only made things worse for Grandfather and me. We realized that the fiesta would be an even bigger embarrassment now, and that the shame for Grandfather would be much, much greater.

I was neglecting my school work but I didn't care. I could make it up after the fiesta, I thought—if there was an "after." I never liked to think of that time; I never knew how it would be. The world might come to an end for Grandfather and me after the fiesta. I had a deep feeling about it—the way I used to feel when I was very young and thought I might die tonight, and I would try to do something enjoyable like read a story in bed before I went to sleep. This time, now, was much better though, because the enjoyable thing before the end of the world was being with the widow. No matter how depressed or frightened I felt after being with Grandfather, I would forget this and get the good feeling again as soon as I was close to the widow. Just seeing her and then touching her hand made everything change. Toward the end, I would rush to her house and grab her immediately and begin to kiss her, urging her to "Hurry. Hurry. Please hurry," while she laughed and pushed my hands away and said, *"Nené, nené!* There is time. There is always time."

One night Grandfather was so depressed that I stayed with him longer than usual. I left for the widow's finally, and ran all the way. A moment after I'd turned the corner of her street I saw a man coming down the steps of her house, a big man whom I recognized immediately. It was Manolín, in his beret and his big bear coat. I was so shocked I stopped running, and then stopped walking. Manolín! What was Manolín doing here? I thought of Grandfather suddenly. Had Grandfather planned this? I cursed him before I could stop myself. Then I remembered how Grandfather had looked when I left him a few minutes ago, and I asked him to forgive me in my mind. But why this, I kept thinking. Why my girl? Hasn't Manolín got enough with the two he brought?

Manolín came down the steps and was walking toward the curb, in the same sloppy, waddling way that he'd walked on the pier and downtown at the Lyceum when I'd seen him going to rehearsal. No one was allowed to see the rehearsals—not even Grandfather.

Manolín couldn't see me of course. He walked to

the curb to cross the street just as a car came down the other way. He saw it, but kept on walking. When the driver of the car began to blow his horn frantically, Manolín stepped right in front of the car. I knew he saw it, because he was staring right at it. The car swerved toward the curb, but Manolín moved back with it, and then leaped away just as it was about to hit him. He made a long, one-footed leap that was sudden and exciting—although I wasn't thinking that at the time—and then kept on leaping until he reached the other side of the street.

I heard the driver cursing as he passed me, and I agreed with him. I had been cursing Manolín myself, in anger and relief. This stupid trick that he'd just played was a variation of a game I'd read about in Spanish novels. It was played by the *golfos,* the street urchins of Madrid, in imitation of the great bullfighters. On a main thoroughfare the player would dart out into the middle of the street and stand directly in the path of an oncoming car, swerve as it swerved—to hold his place in its path—and then leap nimbly aside just before the almost certain moment of contact. As the car sped by him, the *golfo* would strike the graceful pose of a bullfighter passing a charging bull with his cape, and the curses of the driver would be his own particular *olés.*

It was stupid of these poor tragic kids, but it was criminal of Manolín, I thought now. The anger I'd felt on seeing him come out of the widow's house was doubled at the thought of this criminal, risky thing. He'd almost lost us our whole fiesta. That was all we'd need—Manolín hurt or killed. I was so angry at him that I started to run to the widow's house. I couldn't think of anything, and of course I couldn't remember how graceful his leaping had been. That should have been a hint to me, that graceful, light leaping, and I was to remember it later.

I rang the widow's bell hard and long, and started shouting about Manolín as soon as I was in her rooms, about what was he doing here, about what a fool he was, didn't she know what a fool he was, didn't she know? She only stared at me. She was wearing her black dress, but she had her hair down. The comb was in her hand. When I said was it Grandfather who had arranged it for them, she grabbed my arm and shook me and then pushed me back on the couch.

"For that you ought to be slapped," she said in a low voice. "For that. For insulting that noble man."

"I didn't mean it," I said. I had stopped shouting and felt very tired. "I didn't believe it. Ever."

"Manolín came to get what you get. Just what you get. The same," the widow said. She stopped for a minute and then sat down beside me. "But he didn't get it, *nené,*" she said in a softer voice, and put her arm around me. "No." She pressed me to her. "No."

"Well," I started to say, apologetically, "I know that you're——"

"He saw me at the hall this afternoon, and insisted on walking home with me. Insisted. I didn't let him in, of course, but when he rang the bell tonight I had to let him come in for a moment. If only to talk to him and put the truth on things."

"You shouldn't have to explain to me," I said. "You truly shouldn't."

"I wanted to put the truth on things for you, too. Especially in regard to your Grandfather."

"I was foolish to say that. So foolish."

"Yes," she said calmly, but when I looked up at her she was smiling, and she was very, very nice to me that night.

Hours later, when I came out into the street and suddenly remembered the incident of Manolín and the car, I was feeling so happy and benign that I just couldn't be angry at Manolín. I had been planning to tell Mr. Gomez about the car—or have Grandfather tell him—if only to see that he warned Manolín and made certain that it wouldn't happen again, but now I knew that I wouldn't do that. I wouldn't do anything that would cause anger. The time was very short, and I would just have to trust to luck. I hoped Manolín wouldn't try that crazy stunt again or, if he did, that nothing happened to him; but I wouldn't tell Mr. Gomez or Grandfather.

Poor Manolín, I thought. He probably feels just as depressed at the way things turned out as we all do. The car on the street tonight might have reminded him of the game he played as a kid, and he acted instinctively. It was a terrible thing to do, but he must have had his moment of pleasure—if only in memory. No, I thought. I won't tell Mr. Gomez about it, and I certainly won't tell Grandfather.

The last time Grandfather and I were really together before the fiesta was that Thursday afternoon when we went to New York to rent a suit of tails. Grandfather had never worn tails in this country, and this should have been a wonderful occasion. Instead we were both very sad and full of doom. We knew the fiesta was really coming off now, and to us it seemed that we were already in the middle of disaster.

Grandfather tried on a very fine-looking coat with shining lapels and long tails. He threw back his shoulders and wore it well.

"I will look fine in my coffin," he said to me in Spanish. "Yes."

"What did he say?" the man said.

"He said it looks fine," I told him.

"He looks very good in it," the man said. "He knows something about tails."

"Oh, yes," I said proudly, very proudly. "He used to be a headwaiter."

Grandfather chose that fine suit and we took it with us. We bought Grandfather a dress shirt and a white bow tie, and then went straight home. Grandfather had to be at headquarters again that night, and Grandmother was making him take a nap every afternoon. This was a good idea, we thought, because, as Grandfather said, it did make him forget for a while.

I knew that this would be our last time alone before the fiesta, and I worried about how the good-by would go. As we got nearer to home, I tried to think of some easy way to do it—just so that Grandfather or I wouldn't get emotional. I didn't have to worry, though. It went off very well. When we reached his door Grandfather took the small package from me and held out his hand.

"Until Saturday night, *hijo,"* he said. "I will look for you."

"I'll be there, Grandfather," I said, and I pressed his hand.

The next day, Friday, I began to feel real tension. I wouldn't be able to see Grandfather, and I couldn't see the widow tonight. Her sister and niece had come in for the fiesta and were staying with her. I tried to catch up on some homework, but I could not put my mind to it. I went to a movie at night, but it was very lonely. I went to the widow's neighborhood and walked by her house, but the lights were all out and I didn't see anybody. When I got home the family was in bed, even my father.

Mother told me the next morning that Grandfather had fainted at home the night before. Before I could say anything, she said, "Oh, no, don't worry. He's not giving up. Don't look like that. You know how stubborn he is, how terribly stubborn. He won't give up."

I didn't say anything. I was surprised myself at how shocked I had been to hear of something happening to Grandfather now. I knew that tonight was going to be a fiasco, but I didn't want Grandfather to quit. He mustn't quit now. He was almost at the end. He had to go through with it. I knew that Grandfather felt the same way.

"Be sure to stay close to your grandfather tonight," my mother was saying.

"I will. Don't worry." I thought of my coming home with Grandfather—alone, in a taxi, just as we had from the ship. Tonight Grandmother, Mother and all my aunts would be there, but I still thought that Grandfather and I would have to come home alone.

I had a headache, and I started taking aspirin early that morning. I had a bottle hidden in my bookcase because Mother didn't want me to take "drugs." It wouldn't have mattered today, I thought. The whole family had begun preparing for the fiesta right after breakfast, and I was able to keep to myself without anybody noticing.

Mother and my sister had bought new dresses for tonight, and they worked for hours on their hair. My older brother was wearing a tux for the first time, and father's tux had been dry-cleaned. The rest of us boys were all wearing our best. The only time the preparations stopped for a moment was when Mother and my older brother went to church to light two candles to Saint Anthony for Grandfather's success. As the oldest in the house, I was left to watch the dinner on the stove.

I went to the hall before the others. I used the excuse of having to see Grandfather, but I really wanted to get away from the holiday rushing. I was willing to miss the taxi ride for that. I felt light-headed from taking so many aspirins and eating so little, but my headache was gone and when I got to the hall I felt strangely calm.

It was crowded already, even though there was still an hour to go. I went backstage and saw Grandfather. He was surrounded by a lot of important-looking people in full evening dress, and he looked worried and gray, but he was still standing straight and tall and he looked very dignified in his tails. I waved to him and he smiled and made a sign to me that said, Well, it's here! I nodded and smiled back at him, but didn't go over. I had just wanted him to see that I was there. I could see that he was still in control, no matter how worried he looked.

Standing backstage, I could hear the people coming into the auditorium outside, and after a little I discovered the short passage that led directly into the first box where the officials were to sit. When I went to the box and looked out, I was surprised at how quickly the hall was filling. Eight hundred tickets had been sold, but there seemed to be that many people here already. I took another look about fifteen minutes later and the hall seemed completely filled. There were even some people standing along the walls and at the back of the auditorium.

It might have been because of this or because I was just so nervous, but the time for starting seemed to have come very quickly. I was standing at the back of the box when some of the committee members came walking in from the stage, and I walked quickly back to see if I could see Grandfather. I knew he was to make a speech. Agapito was just coming in, and he stopped me and told me to wait—that Mr. Gomez had ordered quiet backstage and that Grandfather would be coming into the box immediately after his speech. Agapito said he was very nervous now, anyway. That was why I wanted to see him, I thought, but I let Agapito lead me back to the box because the house lights were going out and everything had suddenly become very quiet.

I stood at the back of the box as Grandfather walked onto the lighted stage. There was a sudden burst, then a growing volume of applause—that was their farewell to him, I thought—and Grandfather stood at the center of the stage and bowed, and then stood very quietly until the applause had stopped. He looked truly noble and dignified. Even his voice seemed to have a sudden power, though he wasn't trying to force it.

"Welcome to the twenty-fourth fiesta of La España," he said. "We are truly happy to have so many of our friends here. As you know, every year we try to present a part of the glory of our beloved home country. Tonight we present Manolín, the first, the most Spanish of dancers. Later you can dance yourselves and we will serve refreshments. The Committee and I thank you."

Grandfather bowed and walked quickly off. The applause was strong again, but this time with a note of anticipation. As Grandfather came into the box he pressed my shoulder and whispered, "Will you be all right here?"

"Yes, fine," I said. "I'll be fine." I patted his shoulder as he went to his seat in the front of the box.

The stage lights had gone out and the curtain raised, and a strong single spotlight was now directed onto the center of the bare stage. I took a last look at Grandfather, who was sitting up very straight, and then turned to watch as Manolín came walking slowly through the shadow. There was a rush of applause as he stepped into the light. He seemed to move on this into the first fixed position of a *zapateado*. Standing on his toes, his head thrown back, his hands high, he suddenly looked tall and proud, handsome and brave, the great dancer that he was supposed to be. At the first hush of respectful silence, he began to dance.

His part of the program was to have lasted until ten o'clock, but it was eleven fifteen before it could end.

If I had known the slightest truth about Spanish dancing, I would never have worried about Manolín. Grandfather and I would have been spared all that anxiety. I could have told Grandfather this truth and we two would have remained calm while all the others worried about such conventional things as fatness and overweight.

Manolín was great that night—as great as we had heard. For the truth is that Spanish dancing is a completely individual thing; a matter of intimate pride to the performer, it is his own instrument of expression, and it has the same defiance that the Spaniard shows against death in the bullfight and against God in life. The dance is a duel, and the performer is so engrossed in its technique only because he feels it is a matter of his concern and his alone. The true Spanish dancer can dance alone—often, he needs no music.

His fat could not deter Manolín. The fat was another element to conquer, this time with a dominated technique as the ally, not the foe. The inner genius that had made Manolín a great dancer at the age of fourteen was still strong and burning. It fought through to expression easily; the fat was disciplined. We were seeing a big Manolín instead of a thin one; that was the only difference.

He danced *zapateados, flamencos,* and many classical and folk dances. A quiet, effective guitar was his only accompaniment, and in one magnificent dance he used only the rhythm of his own fingers and heels to guide him. Between dances his big body slumped with growing exhaustion, and he stared coldly at the big enthusiastic audience that applauded with growing fervor every time. Toward the end his arrogance seemed to diminish a little and he nodded and smiled two or three times. Then he would move into position for the next dance, his face serious and withdrawn from the hushed crowd.

He was a great artist, and alone, and he made Grandfather's fiesta the biggest triumph that La España ever had.

The next day Grandfather's house was crowded with people who still wanted to talk about the wonder of Manolín and about the great intelligence Grandfather had shown in getting him. The Spanish paper had written up the fiesta on the front page, and the *Times* and the *Brooklyn Eagle* carried big stories about it. It was going to be in all the papers of the world, my uncle said, because the fact that Manolín was back in form was such big news.

"And after all our worrying!" my young Aunt Elvira said.

There was one good thing about all the talking. Nobody said I told you so. Nobody could say that truly in front of Grandfather, because nobody else had had the wisdom or the inspiration to see how wonderfully things would turn out. It had all been Grandfather's. He listened to everybody, now, and looked calm and happy, but he didn't say much. He didn't drink anything either, in spite of all the toasting.

Grandmother didn't want him to, and he didn't complain or protest. When I came in, we had only had a chance to shake hands—I couldn't think of anything to say suddenly—but then, when I was sitting next to him, he reached his hand over and pressed it on mine and held it there.

Mother came over to talk to Grandfather while I was sitting there, and after she had kissed him and congratulated him again she said, "Now you'll be able to rest, Papa, and the boy can get back to his school work."

"Oh, no," Grandfather said. "Just one more day. We have one thing more to do tomorrow." He looked at me. "Yes?"

"Oh, yes, Grandfather!" I said eagerly. When Mother said that so definitely, I'd felt very sad. "Yes."

"Tomorrow at headquarters at the same time, then?" Grandfather said when we were leaving. He pressed my hand very hard.

"I'll be there, Grandfather," I said.

On our way home Mother kept talking about how bad Grandfather looked and how glad she was that all this was over. I thought Grandfather looked bad, too, but it made me feel very depressed when I thought about "all this" being over.

I had an idea of what it was we were going to do, but next afternoon at headquarters when Grandfather told me that we had a check to deliver to the widow, I acted surprised and very pleased. I *was* very pleased.

Grandfather still didn't look well, but he acted quietly content. He stood by the desk for a moment after locking it, as if he had remembered something. Then he began to take the desk key off his ring. "I won't have need of this now," he said.

"But, Grandfather, the next fiesta! The next big one. You're going to be doing that."

Grandfather stared at me for a moment and then smiled. "And will you be working with me on the next fiesta?"

"Of course," I said. "I don't think you need me, but I'll be working with you. Yes."

Grandfather was still smiling as he shook his head. "All right," he said with a sigh. "Good." He left the key on his ring.

On our way out he put his arm around my shoulder. "Your grandmother doesn't think there should be any more fiestas for me," he said. "This morning she told me that I should resign myself to being an old man. That I should truly retire and not do any more foolish things."

"It wasn't a foolish thing," I said. "It was the greatest fiesta La España ever had. Everybody knows that."

"Yes, we did a good thing," Grandfather said. He pressed my shoulder. "*La pareja*—the good pair! And now it's done."

"But there'll be more. There'll be more, Grandfather."

I hated the use of the past tense in all this. I knew this fiesta was over, but I wanted Grandfather and all of us to still go on like this, to think of the next fiesta. I knew Mother and Grandmother wanted it all to be over, but I didn't see how Grandfather could let it go so easily.

"You shouldn't retire now, Grandfather," I said. "Not when everything is so good. Enjoy yourself now. Stay and enjoy this good thing."

"Whether I retire or not—this shouldn't change the good thing you have from the fiesta. No."

"It will, Grandfather," I said, and I knew I was blushing. "Even there. It will be different there, too."

"It will be better," Grandfather said. "Better. You will be alone now, and it will be better. And let us finish with this sad talk," he said, without smiling. "Let us think of this afternoon. Only this afternoon. I will leave early," he said, smiling suddenly at me.

"Oh, no, Grandfather," I protested. "No." I really meant it, too. I was very sorry for Grandfather, even though I'd suddenly begun to worry about whether this sad, finished feeling we had would go with us to the widow's. I'd never thought there was any connection between the fiesta ending and the widow and me. I'd thought we'd go on as before, but now that the fiesta end was having such an effect on Grandfather I wondered if it would affect the widow and me. It won't be different when we get there, I thought. It will be the same as ever. And Grandfather will feel better, too.

And it was the same—for the first few moments. The way the widow was dressed, the way we sat in her front room with the cups of hot chocolate in our hands, the way we all tried to talk together—these things were just as before and just as good. But then the sad, finished feeling of something ending, and ending forever, seemed to creep over us and then clamp itself definitely when I heard the widow saying that she was planning to move to Newark to live with her sister. She was talking to Grandfather when she said it and wasn't looking at me, but Grandfather turned his eyes to me sadly when she said it.

I hated that look. I hated that pity. I was angry at them both. For a moment I wished that Grandfather hadn't come. If the widow had said something like that while we were alone, I knew I could have worked on her and gotten her to change her mind. I wished that Grandfather would leave, as he had said he would. I took the wish back right away and wanted to bite my tongue, because Grandfather looked so sick and worried sitting there.

He had just finished his hot chocolate and was reaching over to put the empty cup on the table, but his hand began to tremble so that he could barely make it. The widow reached out to put the saucer right, and then touched Grandfather's hand kindly. She gripped it tightly as he suddenly slumped forward. I had stood up when I saw his hand trembling, and I was moving over to him when he fell like that. The widow had gripped his shoulder, and we lifted him up to a sitting position. He was very red and then got very white, and his hands were clenched tightly against his chest. His mouth was open and his eyes were shut, but he was murmuring, "Home. Home."

"A wet towel!" the widow said to me. "Quickly!"

"It's only a faint, Don José," I heard her say to him as I rushed for a towel. "Yes, Don José. . . ."

When I brought the towel, she had loosened Grandfather's tie and was unbuttoning his shirt. Grandfather still looked very white, but his mouth was not open as before and his eyes were clear.

"Home. I must get home," he kept saying as the widow sponged his face and head with the towel. "I must get home. *A casa. A casa.*"

"You must rest," the widow said. "Don't say foolish things. Don't think them. You must rest here. It's only a faint, Don José. It will pass."

Grandfather held her hand where she was sponging his cheek. "No, this isn't foolishness, *nena,*" he said. "You know that. You know I must be home. I must be home."

"*Vaya,* Don José!" she said, and made an impatient face. "Please." She sponged a little more and then handed me the towel. "I'll only be a moment. Now wait," she said to my Grandfather. She patted his cheek and went into the back rooms, and I heard her going down the stairs, but even before she'd left the apartment Grandfather had sat up straight and was starting to button his shirt.

"Grandfather, if it's only a faint, why don't you . . ." I started to say. "Shouldn't you . . . ?"

Grandfather shook his head slowly. He didn't look at me, he was concentrating so. I helped him button his shirt. I left the last button open and pulled his tie up to cover it. He pointed to his hat. When I hesitated, he pushed me gently and I picked it up and put it on his head. He adjusted it slowly and then held his arms up to me. I saw how white and tired he looked. I held his arms and pulled him up and he leaned heavily against me for a moment, but then steadied himself. We started toward the door because he had started stepping toward it. I picked up my hat as I passed the sideboard.

Grandfather walked very slowly but steadily, and

we went down the short flight of stairs in the hall without any trouble. I kept wondering where the widow was. Grandfather opened one of the two doors in the vestibule himself, so that I could handle the other, and we went out to the front steps. The widow came running after us just as we made the last step.

"Sit down, Don José," she said. "Sit down, please." She took Grandfather's other arm. "I've called for a taxi. You must rest. Rest."

"No, *nena*. Many thanks for the call," Grandfather said. He was leaning heavily against me and spoke very slowly. "Now, go upstairs. This must not be dramatic. Many thanks again." He reached for her hand.

The widow gripped his hand and stared at him for a moment. Then she bent and kissed it, and I saw that the tears were running down her cheeks as she turned to go. When I raised my hand to my own face instinctively, I felt that it was wet and that I had been crying for a long time.

In the taxi, Grandfather sat back with his head resting in the corner. I didn't want to disturb him by talking, but I took one of his hands in mine and kept patting it softly as we rode.

Grandmother met us at the door. She looked very stern but she didn't scold Grandfather. She took his arm and put it around her and held him on the other side.

"All right. All right," she said. "It's only a faint. You'll rest now. You'll rest and be all right."

"No, loved one," Grandfather said. He turned to look at Grandmother. "It isn't a faint. No."

Grandmother looked very worried for a moment,

but she lowered her eyes and said, "We'll see. We'll see," in a calm voice.

We went very slowly because Grandfather was leaning heavily. We went into the dining room from the hall—it was the nearest room—and over to the couch. Grandfather sat down and we took off his hat and coat. Grandmother fixed an extra pillow for him and he lay back. I lifted his feet up.

All during this time he was breathing very heavily but his eyes were open and clear, and when Grandmother said, "I'll go down and call Dr. Ramirez," and started to move away, Grandfather reached for her hand and said, "No, don't go. Wait a moment."

Grandmother took his hand and put her other hand against his cheek, and he looked up at her and said, "Just one moment more," and closed his eyes and seemed to lean his face against her hand just as the heavy breathing stopped after one long, long, stuttering sigh.

We could hear the sigh go out, and then nothing. We stood there. I went to touch Grandmother's shoulder, but stopped when she said, "José." She was still staring down at Grandfather. She said, "José," in the same way again, and then pushed his head up gently. "The glass!" she said to me without looking around.

I ran and brought the hand mirror and Grandmother held it to Grandfather's lips. There was no mist. She rubbed it against her dress and held it there again. This time she held it longer, but still there was no mist. When she handed it back to me she turned and I saw that she wasn't crying, but her face looked more worried and softer than I had ever seen it.

I watched as she folded Grandfather's hands on

his chest and then bent to undo his tie. She seemed to remember something suddenly, and stopped and re-did the tie neatly in the big knot that Grandfather had always liked. Then she reached up and pulled the narrow black ribbon out of her hair and, slipping it under Grandfather's chin, tied it around at the top of his head.

She did everything slowly but calmly, and I didn't want to cry in front of her. When she turned to look at me again, I tried to say something but couldn't think, and then I remembered and said, "We were at headquarters when it happened. There was nobody else there."

Grandmother nodded and patted my cheek tenderly. "Thank you. We won't tell anyone else the truth."

"It's true, Grandmother."

"Yes, I know," she said, but I could see by the absent-minded way in which she nodded that she hadn't even been listening to me. She didn't believe the lie about headquarters. She knew we had been at the widow's—she must have guessed it, somehow—and I was sure of this in a moment when I saw her staring down at Grandfather with the same look of tenderness and patience that she had just given me. This was Grandmother's *forgiving* look—I had seen it often as a child—and she was forgiving Grandfather now as she had just forgiven me.

There's nothing to forgive there, Grandmother, I wanted to whisper to her. Nothing. Nothing. And then I felt so bitterly angry that I suddenly wanted to grab her arm and turn her to me so that I could shout it at her. Grandfather never did anything wrong at the widow's, I wanted to shout. Never. Never! He never did. How can you keep thinking that? How can you keep thinking that he did? There's nothing to forgive Grandfather for. Nothing, I tell you!

I wanted to shout it—I could feel my heart beating fast in anticipation and my hand was ready to jump out—but I knew that I wouldn't do it. It was going to stay in my head—all of it. I couldn't say anything like that in front of Grandfather, and then, when Grandmother suddenly bent down and kissed Grandfather and patted his cheek as she had mine, I could see how full of love she was for him, and I thought: let her think what she wants. I wasn't angry anymore. Let her think what she wants forever, I thought. So long as she loves him, let her think what she wants.

When she stood up and looked at me, she reached over and patted my arm. "Now, go get your mother," she said in her usual calm voice, "but don't run. Give me a little time with him alone."

# *Chapter Six*

In the years after my grandfather's death, Grandmother lost much of her bitterness. She never came to like America or its way of life, but she knew now that she would never go back to Spain and she was resigned to spending her last years here. Grandmother had security and comfort during this time because my uncle Joe, her son, had a very good job, and there is a kind of ironic justice in this. Joe was a certified public accountant, and it was Grandmother who had insisted that he go to high school and be kept out of the cigar business.

She had sacrificed and planned to send Joe through high school and then to business school at night. Lots of people in the colony—and even some of the family—objected to this. They felt it was out of character, not Spanish. They said, if Joe was to be educated why not make him a doctor or a lawyer—give him a respectable profession. Grandmother said no; that this was a business country and a money country. "It will always be like that," she said. "I want Joselito to have steady work. That's why I want him to be in a business that has to do with money."

It had turned out just that way. Joe began to make good money even before he'd had his certificate and, after he'd become a C. P. A., he began to make a fine salary. He was only twenty-five, but he was making more money than any man in the colony except Agapito Lopez. Joe married an American girl and, when his firm transferred, he moved to Boston. He quit the Spanish society, La España, and broke all contacts with the colony except for Grandmother and, when people criticized him for all that—even Mother and my aunts didn't like it—Grandmother still defended Joe. "His father had the friendship and respect of everyone," she said, "and what did it avail us? No, I think Joselito is smart. I think he will succeed here."

Grandmother didn't seem to mind the coldness that developed toward her after this. She still had the respect of everyone, of course, but even her oldest friends had grown a little cool. Mother and my aunts, too, seemed to resent the way that Grandmother had "pushed" Joe, but Grandmother never minded on either count.

At that period in her life she didn't seem to care for the company of adults and was concentrating on us, her grandchildren. During the last years of her life we were closer to Grandmother then we had ever been before. We knew her for the first time and, since those were the years of the great Depression, Grandmother's advice and economic help were more than welcome to those of us who were about to become job hunters.

I was lucky enough to still have a year to go in college, but Grandmother had something for me, too. She knew that I wanted to be a writer and was interested in Spain, and so she would often sit and tell me long stories about her life there—stories I knew she'd seldom told anyone, and certainly not in the way she told them to me.

The night she told me this particular story, we were "watching" each other. I was home in bed with a cold, and Grandmother had come to stay with me. "It is implied," she said, "that you need watching." I had gotten the cold by walking two miles through the rain after having a bad quarrel with my girl. "But the truth is," Grandmother said, "that you're supposed to watch me. Those bourgeois fools of my daughters!"

Mother and the aunts were always worrying about Grandmother's being alone, particularly in this time when she seemed so removed from them and her old friends. "What part of life these bourgeois don't see, they don't understand," Grandmother said. She used the strong Spanish word *burgueses*. "They feel their own fright for us. Now, what is this new thing, this thing of you and the girl?"

I told her about the quarrel and getting wet, and that I was through. "I'm giving up the fight," I said.

"Oh no, you're not. No." She shook her head without looking at me. She had brought a bottle of brandy and was pouring some into two small snifters. She handed me one of them, and then, delicately balancing her glass, lay down beside me on the big couch. She pulled the afghan up over her legs. She had on a black taffeta skirt, a black blouse and a high, bizarre collar, and she smelled of a light perfume and the strong, deep incense that she still used in her apartment in spite of all protests. She was seventy-two but, as you looked at her, you thought that age has a distinctive beauty of its own.

"Sip it," she said, tasting her brandy and leaning back against the pillows. "It's good for you." She watched me for a moment and then nodded. "There's something about good brandy that makes you never want to die," she said. She held the glass to her nose and then took another sip. Without turning to me, she began to talk.

"I never told this story to anyone. I always wanted to tell it to you," she said, "and I'm going to tell it to you now because it's about a man who gave up the fight—as you phrase it." She stared at the brandy in her small glass for a moment. "When I was very young," she said, "I was very beautiful. You've probably heard some stories about it, but they could never really tell it.

"I couldn't go out to the beach very much, even though I loved to bathe. I was followed and courted and proposed to—that is permitted in Spain, you know—and I was very shy and didn't like it. I never wanted to go out into the street without my father. Even when I was with my *dueña,* the men would come up to me. That is permitted in Spain, too.

"I was beautiful—very, very beautiful. I used to walk across my room toward the big mirror and love myself when I reached there. I used to do that every time I was dressed to go out. And I had a thin white nightgown that I also used to put on at night especially to do that." Grandmother smiled and took a sip of the brandy. "Yes," she said, and stared for a moment.

"I had much admiration from men—and many suitors—but I didn't seem to want that. I loved my beauty and I loved myself, and I didn't want that beauty to be spoiled. Marriage seemed to do that—even love seemed to do that. You could not separate the two.

"I married your grandfather in a strange way," she said. "He'd been married to my best friend, and she had died just a year after the marriage. We'd grown very close while I'd been caring for her, and he was a very kind and soft man. You knew him when he'd become bitter, but he was very gentle and kind when we were young. He didn't seem to spoil my beauty," Grandmother said, "but then, he didn't seem to make it his either. It seemed all mine still, and it was a little dead now.

"I was restless, and so I was glad to go to Tangier when he had a better position offered to him there. Your mother was born when we'd been there only a short time, and there was a smallpox epidemic at the same time, and I got it. I should have been glad," Grandmother said, "because my daughter and my husband were spared, but I couldn't feel that. I was miserable!

"The cursed pox seemed to concentrate in my face—in my nose. The stupid fool of a doctor—the best in Tangier—told me that I would probably lose my nose. He was very concerned about it, but he was still very definite." My grandmother rubbed her nose. It was still a beautifully shaped patrician nose.

"He had to take the baby away," she said, "and he sent your grandfather to live in a hotel. Then the fool went away himself. He was very frightened. I was frightened too, but not for the same reasons! I wasn't afraid of dying, and I didn't miss my daughter or your grandfather. I was frightened of losing my nose. I was frightened of having my beauty spoiled—before it became alive, before it had lived for me."

She sipped at her drink, and then smiled without looking at me. "You know, a man may look at a woman's legs first, or at her bust and hips, but it always seemed to me that beauty is in the eyes, in the face. I always thought of mine like that anyway—even though my body was beautiful. The face seemed a mirror, a center, and the eyes looked right at you." She turned to me this time as she smiled. "I'd been looking at mine a lot, you see. Take away that nose, I thought, and there would be a horror. I thought of my face as a mask, as becoming a horrible mask, with two holes in it!

"I couldn't get any consolation out of religious thoughts, out of thinking of wearing a veil, and I couldn't get any solace out of the fact that your grandfather would always 'love' me. My beauty was going to be spoiled," my grandmother said. "It was going to be spoiled at last, and never in the way I thought."

She took another slow sip of the brandy. "All this was even more horrible," she said, "because it was dark. I was alone and it was night and it was dark. I was used to being alone, but I couldn't stand the darkness. Everything seemed truly horrible, then—as if it were the truth forever.

"Before the maid had left she'd done me a last service. She'd tied my hands to the side of the bed. In smallpox, the danger is that you'll scratch. The sores will grow deeper, and you'll have terrible scars if you survive. So she had really done me a service.

"I lay awake in that dark room with my face a hot torture. The fears and horrors came to me in the dark, and I clenched my hands. I wept, I think. There was a fever, too, and that helped the fear along. It helped the horrors. The worst horror of all was that I was losing my beauty—in the darkness and in the fever. I didn't think of my child; I didn't think of my husband. I didn't even think of whether I'd live or die. I just thought of losing my nose, of all my beauty being spoiled.

"After a few hours—it might have been less than that," she said, "a little Jewish doctor came to see me. He was very young—his beard was still tawny—and he had that calm, quiet dignity that the Semites have in their own country. I thought that he had been sent by my own doctor. I thought that the fool must have had a sudden rush of conscience and sent this young doctor. He wouldn't risk it himself, but he could order someone else. I found out later that it wasn't like that. I found that he had come on his own. He had been admiring me many days before, and when he learned that I was ill with the pox he came up.

"When he came in, and I saw who he was, I became the great 'lady.' I resented being sent a 'second-class' doctor—a doctor that could be spared—and a Semite! I told him to go away. Everything in me burned to ask for some help, but I told him to go away. He smiled at me kindly, and said, 'Please, Señora!' Then, he waited a moment and started to take the cords from my wrists. 'I don't think we're going to need these,' he said. He had a soft, beautiful voice. 'No,' he said. 'No, we won't need these.' He put some ointment on my face, with the same softness as his voice, and the burning itching seemed to soothe at once. Then he gave me a sleeping potion."

My grandmother took a sip at her brandy. She seemed to wet her lips only, but the smile showed how much she enjoyed it.

"I don't know whether I slept very long," she went on, "but it didn't seem very long, and when I awoke it was still very dark. The itching had come back more strongly than ever, and I woke up because there was a pressure holding my wrists down. I must have been trying to bring my hands up to my face. When I opened my eyes, he was sitting at my bedside and holding my wrists—with a light touch, but very strongly. I worked to get my wrists free, but he held on very firmly and smiled softly at me. 'The itching will pass soon,' he said. 'It will pass soon, Señora.'

"I was enraged at this little Semite who sat at my bedside as if he meant to stay. 'Why don't you leave with the others?' I said. 'Aren't you afraid?'

" 'No,' he said, smiling. 'No.' He was holding both my wrists in one of his long-fingered hands and putting some ointment on my face with the other. 'I am not afraid,' he said. 'No.' And his ointment seemed to work again, because the itching stopped and I went to sleep again.

"I woke up when the itching came back. He was still there. As he soothed my pain, I ranted at him. I ranted at that ugly, dignified little Semite. 'Why do you do this?' I said. 'Why do you take such risks?'

" 'Because I love you,' he said with great calm.

" 'And will you love me when I lose my nose—when I am horrible and not beautiful?'

" 'I will love you then, but you will always be beautiful,' he said. 'If you lost your nose, I would be even happy—because you would not be so beautiful and I could be sure of you then. A poor little man like me could have a queen.'

" 'You are a poor little man!' I hissed at him. 'Is that the way you win a woman? Do you wait until she's horrible and ugly and afraid?'

" 'With you, yes,' he said. 'You would not have looked at me twice before. And you will not lose your nose,' he said. 'I promise you that.'

"He'd finished with the ointment, and the itching began to go away again. I slept some more, and awoke to new itching—but he was there again with the soothing ointment. I woke up many times during that night, and he was always there. Toward the morning I slept for a long time.

"When I woke up after that," my grandmother said, "there was a beautiful young girl sitting by the bed. She smiled at me when I woke up and then, when she saw that I was calm, she gave me some soup and washed me. The Jewesses that you see in New York have been corrupted by Russian and German blood, but in Spain and Morocco, you see the pure Jewess. This was a beautiful Esther—the most beautiful girl I had ever seen, shining black hair and eyes, lovely olive skin, a ripe, fruitful body.

"I said to my little man when he came back later, 'You have a very beautiful nurse.' 'Oh, that isn't my nurse,' he said. 'A nurse would be afraid to come.

That is my wife,' he said. 'I ordered her to come.' He smiled at me—a sly smile, I thought.

"He stayed with me all that night, and the girl stayed during the day. He was on his calls during the day, so I don't know when he slept. What I know is that I was never civil to him, and I never thanked him.

"During the fourth night he told me that he thought he could call my own doctor back. The danger had passed and I was safe. I was not to lose my nose. I would not even be scarred, he said.

"I remember that there was no itch at that time, and I felt very calm and even happy—but I could not get myself to thank him. I just stared up at him, and I remember that I opened my lips to ask him about his fee. He seemed to know what I was thinking. 'I have been paid,' he said. Then, he made a little bow to me and said, 'Good night, my queen.' He did not even touch my hand."

My grandmother let the last drops of the brandy slip down onto her lips. She moved her tongue over her lips, and turned to look at me. She looked at me for a long moment. When she turned back, she said, "I was much improved the next day, and I was up in three days. Your grandfather and his friends all congratulated me on my luck. They told me how well and 'beautiful' I looked. But I couldn't believe it," she said. "No. It was true that everything was all right, that I had no scars and that my face was whole—but I seemed plain and cold to myself. I knew myself, too!" She turned to look at me and smiled. "I knew what my beauty was, and it wasn't there, now!

"When I was fully recovered, your grandfather got a short leave—a month, I think—and we planned to sail to Spain for a few weeks' holiday." My grandmother stopped but did not turn to look at me. "My beauty began to come back," she said, "on the last morning in Tangier. I could feel it as soon as I had decided a certain thing, and I saw it and felt it through the whole morning. I had decided something very definitely, and when I packed I packed my own things separately from the baby's and your grandfather's. Then, I dressed myself in my most beautiful clothes and I walked toward the mirror. I knew that I was beautiful!

"I told your grandfather to take the child to the pier with him, that I wanted to say good-by to my nurse. I used the danger of infection as an excuse for not taking the child. Then, I took a carriage and went to the home of the little man in the Jewish quarter. I found that his house was a clean little house on a corner, but he wasn't there. His wife was there and she seemed to sense why I had come because she did not ask me in. I said something silly and conventional, and then left and went back to the hotel for my trunks.

"When I was coming out again I caught sight of him standing on the corner and looking at me. He had come to have a last look—from afar. If he had been at his house, or had later come up to me, I would have stayed with him forever."

Grandmother stared at her glass, and then turned to put it on the floor. When she turned back to me, I had got up on my elbow and was watching her. She reached out her hand and rubbed my cheek. "You